A Vanished World
The dinosaurs of western Canada

Managing editor: Viviane Appleton
Maps and diagrams: Edward Hearn
Photographs of paintings: Susanne M. Swibold
Design: Jacques Charette and Associates Ltd.
Typesetting: Pierre Des Marais Inc.
Colour separations and printing:
Herzig-Somerville Ltd.

A Vanished World
The dinosaurs of western Canada

by Dale A. Russell

photographs by Susanne M. Swibold
paintings by Eleanor M. Kish

Natural History Series, No. 4

National Museum of Natural Sciences
National Museums of Canada, Ottawa

© Crown copyrights reserved

Natural History Series No. 4
National Museum of Natural Sciences
National Museums of Canada
Ottawa, Canada
1977

Catalogue No. NM 95-17/4

Available by mail from the
National Museums of Canada
Marketing Services
Ottawa, Canada
K1A 0M8

English edition ISBN 0-660-00011-3
                 ISSN 0317-5642

French edition ISBN 0-660-00012-1
                ISSN 0317-5677

Printed in Canada

Publications in the Natural History Series:

1 *A Guide to the Freshwater Sport Fishes of Canada*, by D.E. McAllister and E.J. Crossman. Illustrated by C.H. Douglas. 1973.

2 *Rocky Mountain Wild Flowers*, by A.E. Porsild. Illustrations by Dagny Tande Lid. Published jointly with Parks Canada, Department of Indian and Northern Affairs, 1974.

3 *Mount Revelstoke National Park Wild Flowers*, by James H. Soper and Adam F. Szczawinski. Published jointly with Parks Canada, Department of Indian and Northern Affairs, and the British Columbia Provincial Museum, 1976.

4 *A Vanished World: The Dinosaurs of Western Canada*, by Dale A. Russell. Photographs by Susanne M. Swibold, paintings by Eleanor M. Kish. 1977.

5 *A Guide to the Jellyfish of Canadian Atlantic Waters*, by C.T. Shih. 1977.

Toutes ces publications sont aussi en vente en français

English edition
distributed by
Hurtig Publishers
10560 105 Street
Edmonton, Alberta

ISBN 0-88830-147-2

Contents

Introduction, 7

I Fossil Skeletons, 11

II Shadows of the Past, 21
The Great Trough, 23
Mileposts in Time, 26
The Geography of a Vanished World, 29

III A Park for Dinosaurs, 35
Prairie Badlands, 37
From Sediments to Landscapes, 42
Petrified Vestiges of Life, 48
Reptilian Giants, 56
A Matter of Survival, 62

IV Environments on an Ancient Delta, 65
The Cliffs of Drumheller, 67
Wetland Forests, 72
Denizens of Ancient Swamps, 81
A Coastal Plain, 84
An Ancient Forest of Broad-leaved Trees, 85
Hardwoods and Dinosaurs, 91

V The Last Dinosaurs, 101
A Trough That Ceased to Sink, 103
Life on a Subtropical Floodplain, 112
A Doomed Panorama, 121

VI The End of an Era, 123
On the Land, 125
In the Sea, 127
The Testimony of the Earth, 128
From the Depths of Space, 130

References, 135

Dagmar Galt

Dale A. Russell

Elected to Phi Beta Kappa on graduating with a Bachelor of Arts, Dale Russell received National Science Foundation fellowships to attend the University of California at Berkeley for his Masters, and Columbia University in New York for his Ph.D. in vertebrate palaeontology. After completing a postdoctoral fellowship at Yale University in 1965, he was appointed to the National Museum of Canada to conduct research on the large reptiles that once lived in Canada. Dr. Russell has worked in the field from the Arctic to the Gulf of Mexico, and has studied many collections of large fossil reptiles on this continent and in eastern and western Europe. The author is now chief of the Palaeobiology Division of the National Museum of Natural Sciences, Ottawa.

Susanne M. Swibold

Susanne Swibold received a Master of Fine Arts in painting, drawing and photography from the University of Michigan. She has taught photography at the Banff School of Fine Arts and in the Department of Fine Arts at Concordia University, Montreal. Ms. Swibold has exhibited in Canada and the United States, and more recently at the Musée d'Art contemporain in Montreal. Her photographic projects have included work for the National Film Board, the National Museums of Canada, and Parks Canada. Assignments in photography and documentary films have taken her from the Nahanni National Park of the Northwest Territories to the Galápagos Islands of Ecuador. In 1973 Ms. Swibold received the Canada Council's Senior Arts Grant in photography. At present she is living in Canmore, Alberta.

Eleanor M. Kish

A professional artist in portraiture and landscape, Eleanor Kish studied in California under Ejnar Hansen and Julian Ritter. She has travelled extensively in Canada, the United States and Mexico, and studied for three years at San Miguel de Allende. The Cleveland Museum of Art has exhibited her work. Some of her portraits and scenic reconstructions are on permanent display in Ottawa at the National Museum of Natural Sciences, the National Museum of Man, and the Canadian War Museum. Many Canadians have become familiar with Miss Kish's work through the background paintings she did for the Centennial train and caravans.

Introduction

One may question the value of knowing that a very long time ago many kinds of giant reptiles inhabited that part of the earth which is now Canada. Many other needs are more pressing and of more immediate importance to our well-being. Yet, once these requirements have been at least minimally met, we find that we experience an ever-increasing need to explore our surroundings and manipulate the materials of which they are made. We are fascinated by consistency within the fabric of nature, and are delighted when we are able to predict some previously unsuspected fact as a logical consequence of what we already knew. As a result of this innate quality, mankind has come to realize, among other things, that there were once dinosaurs. The purpose of this volume is to visualize, so far as is possible, the vanished world of Canadian dinosaurs.

Many researchers have devoted a large part of their professional lives to exploring what remains of Canada as it was when the dinosaurs were alive. No one person can adequately translate the available evidence into a popular natural history of that time, and I apologize to my colleagues for the inexactitudes they will surely find here. The rapid accumulation of information will quickly render parts of this text obsolete, but nowhere more rapidly than in our understanding of plant life during the last part of the dinosaurian era. Nevertheless, it is hoped that this work will help others to understand what western Canada may have been like during a very interesting and relatively well documented period of its physical history.

The colour photographs of Susanne M. Swibold provide a visual accompaniment to the text, depicting the beauty of the badlands of western Canada and modern environments similar to those in which their now-barren strata were formed. The photographs are a statement in their own right of her visual interpretation of some of the objects that natural scientists are privileged to study. The artistic merit of the paintings by Eleanor Kish is also evident; hopefully these restorations convey a reasonably accurate impression of environments that none of us can ever see.

Many others have contributed their time and talent to the creation of this work. Among them are Mr. Albert Dugal and Dr. David Jarzen, who gave freely of their botanical expertise, both in the field and in the laboratory. Dr. Frank Simpson generously reviewed the geological content of the manuscript, Dr. Wallace Tucker the astronomical, and Dr. John Ostrom the vertebrate palaeontological. Nevertheless, the responsibility for any errors and misinterpretations must remain mine. Dr. Clair Brown, Dr. Arnold Lewis and Dr. William Gillis provided invaluable assistance in guiding us to native and exotic vegetation growing along the Gulf Coast of the United States. Mr. and Mrs. Gilles Danis located sites of geologic interest for the photographic party in Alberta and Saskatchewan. Finally, I acknowledge my gratitude to the people living on the Canadian prairies who have allowed me, and other earth scientists, to study the fragments of the sedimentary record exposed on their lands, and who share a common interest in the antiquity of Canada.

Ottawa
14 May 1974

I Fossil Skeletons

The rigours of the Canadian climate are very familiar to those of us who live within this vast northern region of North America. Yet our climate has not always been as relatively mild as it is today. Only a few tens of thousands of years ago, along what are now approximately the borders of Canada, stretched the edges of a continuous sheet of continental ice that was several thousand feet thick. For reasons as yet poorly understood, the climate became warmer and drier about 12 thousand years ago. The ice sheet fragmented and disintegrated, leaving behind a mantle of glacially transported sands and gravels, as well as sediments deposited in streams and lakes of melting glacial ice. Mankind first entered North America from eastern Asia, across a Siberia–Alaska land bridge, then, more recently, from western Europe, across the Atlantic Ocean. The boundaries of new nation-states then began to take shape on this continent.

Rivers reoccupied old stream valleys on the prairies of western Canada after the ice retreated. They eroded through the mantle of glacial debris deposited on the valley floors, to reveal much more ancient sediments. The summers became too hot and dry for forests to grow. Because the hold of plant

The western interior of Canada, showing the edges of the great trough and the present boundary between forest and prairie. Badland areas are located along the banks of the Red Deer River in the vicinity of Drumheller and Dinosaur Provincial Park.

cover on the land is now so tenuous, the ancient sediments are frequently exposed along the sides of river valleys, below the level of the prairies. During the summer of 1874, geologists of Her Majesty's North American Boundary Commission, working westwards along the Forty-ninth Parallel from the Lake of the Woods, reached the valley of Rocky Creek in the original Northwest Territories (Morgan Creek, Saskatchewan). From the ancient sediments exposed there they discovered the first dinosaur bones to be collected in Canada.

As field parties of the Geological Survey of Canada continued to explore the western regions of the prairies, they found other large, isolated, and usually shattered bones of dinosaurs weathering out of valley walls, particularly where the sediments were composed of sands and silts of ancient coastal plains. In other areas, where the ancient sediments were formed from muds deposited beneath long-vanished seas, the shells of extinct marine organisms were found. All of these creatures had lived during the last part of that period in the history of the earth which has come to be known as the Mesozoic, or the age of dinosaurs. Thus, through

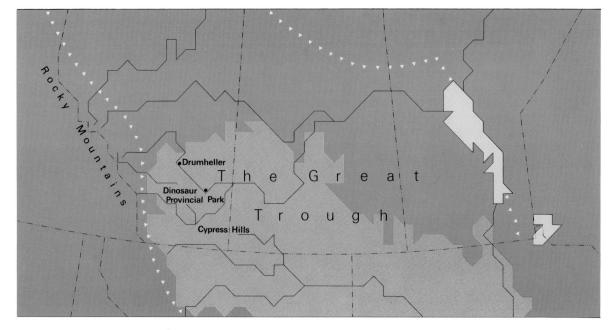

*Lower Horseshoe Canyon
Formation along the Red Deer River
near Drumheller, Alberta
(S72-3969)*

rents torn by rivers into the blanket of ice-age rubble, a vast and much more ancient deposit of deltaic and shallow marine sediments could be seen, extending between the Lake of the Woods and the Rocky Mountains.

In 1884 and 1889, geologists entered the valley of the Red Deer River in central Alberta from the west, and explored it to its junction with the South Saskatchewan. They found two great areas where the ancient deltaic sediments were exposed in sloping valley walls, which were eroded into extensive and intricately sculptured badlands and littered with broken fragments of dinosaur bones. A few bones were laboriously hauled out of the badlands by the collectors themselves or were carried out on horses. They were packed in boats and wagons and transported, none too carefully, to railway stations and on to the Museum of the Geological Survey in Ottawa. Near the turn of the century the more southerly, and larger, of the two badland areas was sampled for the fossil reptiles it contained. Although their collections indicated the presence of several different kinds of dinosaurs, the collectors were distracted from rarer, more complete specimens by great quantities of isolated well-preserved bones. They had no experience in collecting such heavy, fragile objects, and were confronted with great difficulties in carrying them out of the virtually uninhabited badlands.

Ball cactus, Dinosaur Provincial
Park (S72-4031)

Such materials as they were able to remove were shipped to the Museum and described. Then the scientists of the Survey turned their attention to exploring other parts of the subcontinent that constituted their area of operation.

The first locality in the United States to produce entire skeletons of dinosaurs in large numbers was discovered in 1877 at Como Bluff, in the Wyoming Territory, within a mile of the Union Pacific Railroad. During the next 12 years, tons of dinosaur bones were collected at this site for Yale's Peabody Museum of Natural History in New Haven, Connecticut, and the National Museum of Natural History in Washington, D.C. In 1897 the American Museum of Natural History in New York also began to search for dinosaur remains in the American west. By 1909 they had completed an important collection of fragmentary dinosaur skeletons from the tributaries of the Missouri River, south of the Forty-ninth Parallel, and could draw on three decades of experience in collecting large, fragile fossil bones.

At about this time an Alberta rancher, after seeing the dinosaur bones on display in the American Museum of Natural History, informed scientists there that large quantities of similar bones could be found on his ranch near Drumheller on the Red Deer River. After a preliminary appraisal in 1909, a party from the American Museum floated down the Red Deer the following year in a large flat-bottomed boat. They began to collect bones from the valley walls 40 miles upstream from Drumheller, loading the specimens into the boat as it moved down the river. The attention of the collectors was again diverted by large quantities of isolated well-preserved bones. Their collections, though large, were of no better quality than some earlier ones made farther downstream. However, in 1911, a complete skeleton of a new kind of duckbilled dinosaur was excavated and shipped to New York. General interest in dinosaurs was such that the Geological Survey of Canada could not ignore the significance of the American Museum's work on the Red Deer.

In 1912 the Survey equipped and fielded a party of experienced collectors in the vicinity of Drumheller, downstream from the group working for the American Museum.

As the Survey group was becoming familiar with the terrain, the other collectors split their camp in order to begin taking up excellent specimens from the second, more southerly, area of badlands on the river 40 miles below Drumheller. Spurred by each other's presence, the collectors searched only for complete materials, such as entire skulls and skeletons. For four years, Survey and American Museum parties strove mightily to obtain as many high-quality specimens as possible. After 1915 the American Museum ceased collecting in Alberta. Field crews from the Museum of the Geological Survey (now the National Museums of Canada), the Royal Ontario Museum, and a few other museums continued to collect along the river in diminishing numbers until the mid thirties.

To date, the skeletal remains of more than 475 dinosaurs, many of them nearly complete, have been recovered from the barren valley walls of the Red Deer River, at a cost of over 15,000 man-days of labour. These remains were taken

from sediments of three distinct
ages. The oldest skeletons belong
to animals that died tens of millions
of years before the end of the dinosaurian era, and the youngest to
animals that lived just before the
extinction of their race. That such
a large collection could be made is
the result of the great extent of
badland areas bounding the river
and the abundance of fossils contained within the sediments exposed there. We also owe much to
the spirit of competition and fair
play that existed between the
collectors working for the American
Museum and those for the Geological Survey. Each stimulated the
other, and provided a goal for the
collectors who followed them. Had
the specimens not been collected
they would have been destroyed
by the elements, which continually
erode the badlands. Over the decades new skeletons are exposed
by the water from rains and melting
snows, and the fossil productivity
of the Red Deer badlands is
renewed.

The valley of the Red Deer River
constitutes the heartland of dinosaur collecting in Canada. Nowhere
else have badlands proven to be so
extensive and so productive of

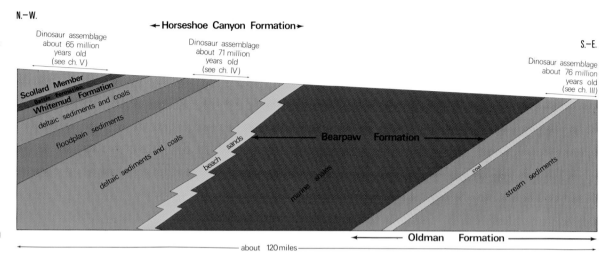

Diagram of the three levels of dinosaur-producing strata on the Red Deer River. The originally nearly horizontal sediments were tipped toward the Rocky Mountains by a sinking of the great trough to the west, along its main axis. The vertical dimension is greatly exaggerated.

N.–W.

←Horseshoe Canyon Formation➤

S.–E.

Dinosaur assemblage
about 65 million
years old
(see ch. V)

Dinosaur assemblage
about 71 million
years old
(see ch. IV)

Dinosaur assemblage
about 76 million
years old
(see ch. III)

Scollard Member

Battle Formation

Whitemud Formation

deltaic sediments and coals

floodplain sediments

deltaic sediments and coals

beach sands

Bearpaw   Formation

marine shales

coal

stream sediments

about 120 miles

Oldman   Formation

Juniper wood on the Alberta prairie
(S72-4128)

dinosaurian remains. Between 1920 and 1962, collectors, most of them from the National Museum of Canada, explored adjacent regions of the prairies for skeletal remains of large fossil reptiles. Specimens were found in the valleys of the Bow, Little Bow and Milk rivers, along the western flanks of the Cypress Hills in southern Alberta, and in the valleys of the South Saskatchewan River, the Frenchman River and Morgan Creek in southern Saskatchewan. However, these collections were not large, and probably signalled the closing phases of the exploration of the Canadian west for dinosaurs. Skeletons will continue to be exposed through the erosion of the prairie badlands, but fewer will be found that belong to previously unknown forms. To the north and east, the ancient sediments containing dinosaur remains are hidden by a nearly uninterrupted blanket of lakes, marshes and forests. To the west, they are broken and crumpled against archaic rocks in the eastern ramparts of the Canadian Rockies.

Since the end of the Second World War, the forests and glacial debris on the plains east of the Rockies have been drilled in the search for oil and other mineral deposits. A great trough of ancient sediments has been found beneath the plains, extending from the mouth of the Mackenzie River in the north to the Gulf of Mexico. These sediments contain a wealth of information about the environments in which the dinosaurs lived.

II Shadows of the Past

The Great Trough

Time is measured in change, whether by the movement of instruments or in the appearance of our bodies. We often feel the need to escape to places where time will not follow, to the solitude of a cathedral or an untouched forest floor. Here, as we contemplate the scope of human existence, we cannot forget that even cathedrals crumble and forests die. The computations of astronomers bear witness to the gradual alteration of constellations as stars move across the firmament. The works of nature and mankind disintegrate and are gone, and nothing endures on the vault of the sky or the surface of the sea. Only the shape of the land seems eternal.

Yet we hear accounts of earthquakes and landslides, the destruction of farmlands through erosion, or problems caused by a blanket of silt left behind by floods. Over the course of centuries the repetition of such events alters the appearance of the land. The crust of the earth itself is not perfectly rigid, and even in its most stable regions slowly rises, bends or sinks with the passing of the aeons. As a region rises, its surface gradually disintegrates before the attacks of wind, water, frost, and ice. The fragments are carried by streams and rivers to regions closer to the level of the sea. If these regions are slowly sinking, many thousands of feet of sediment may accumulate.

The hard parts of plants and animals that die on the surface of a slowly sinking region, or are carried there by wind and running water, will be buried in the accumulating sediments. Should such a region cease to sink and slowly begin to rise, the sediments deposited last will again be dispersed by the elements. Where the plant-cover and soil are broken, the fossilized hard parts of plants and animals once buried in the sediments will reappear at the surface of erosion. Erosion will continue, exposing increasingly older sediments and fossils, as long as the region continues to rise.

The great trough of ancient sediments lying to the east of the Rocky Mountains marks the site of a vast region that was slowly sinking during the last part of the dinosaurian era. Most of the surface of sediment accumulation was below sea level, where volcanic ash and fine muds were carried by wind and water currents from lands along the edge of the inland sea. A long chain of unstable, rising mountain ranges bordered the sea along its entire western shore, from the Arctic Ocean to the Gulf of Mexico. Rivers from these mountains carried enormous volumes of sediment eastwards, building deltas out into the trough. At various times the supply of sediment could not keep pace with the sinking of the trough along its western edge, and the deltas were submerged. At other times, slowly rising ranges altered the courses of rivers, and shed new floods of sediment to form deltas in other regions of the western shore. Then, long after the last dinosaurs died, the surface of the entire trough rose above sea level. We have seen exposures of its ancient sediments along river valleys in Canada, under the mantle of glacial debris.

The glaciers did not extend very far below the Forty-ninth Parallel west of the Lake of the Woods, and the great plains of the United States are largely free of glacial rubble.

The western interior of the United States, showing areas where the floor of the interior sea has been brought to the surface around the edges of the Black Hills and the Colorado Front Range. The southern limit of continental glaciers during the Ice Age is also indicated.

Here the summers are generally hotter than in Canada, and the climate is often more arid. Beneath the western half of the great trough in the United States, vertical movements within the crust of the earth brought ancient sediments to the surface around the flanks of the Black Hills of South Dakota, the Big Horn Mountains of Wyoming, and the Front Ranges of Colorado, and in several other regions. As a result of these crustal movements, sediments that were deposited on the floor of the ancient seaway during the latter part of the dinosaurian era are now widely exposed across the high plains and around the ranges of the eastern Rockies in the United States.

Such sediments encircle the Black Hills uplift in eastern Wyoming and western South Dakota. An earth scientist may explore them alone, beneath the hot, blue canopy of the midsummer sky. Gazing about he would see barren hillsides sculptured by the elements from sediments deposited long ago, when the world was not as it is now. He may reach out and touch the ancient clays, but he will remain forever frustrated by his inability to lift the veil separating his life from their muted origins and to enter the world in which they were formed and he was not. However, in searching the sediments he will find clues that will enable him to probe the current of time.

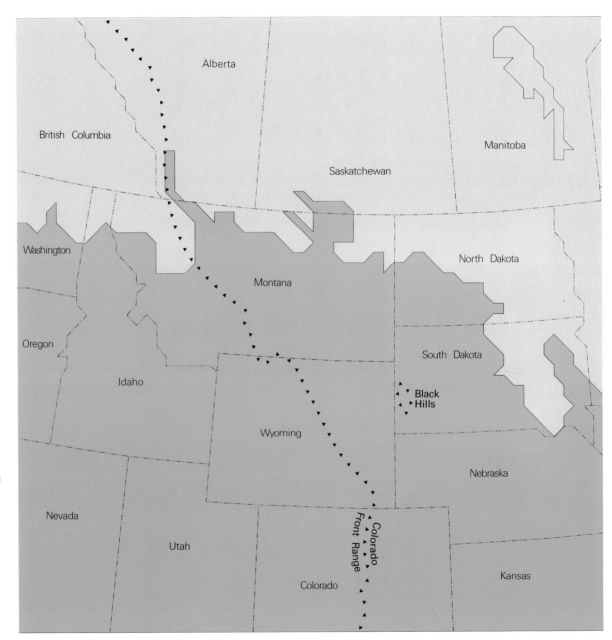

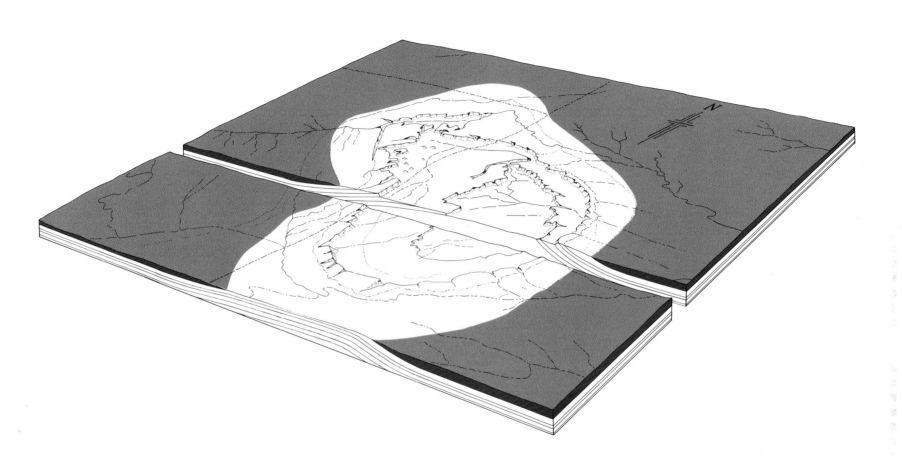

Block diagram of the Black Hills of South Dakota and inclined marine sediments on their flanks

Badlands of marine mudstones on the southwestern edge of the Black Hills

Mileposts in Time

The region was far from land when the particles of clay settled through the water to the bottom of the sea. Although the remains of bottom-dwelling shellfish buried there live at depths of only 200 feet today, a gradual but protracted sinking of the sea floor nevertheless permitted some 3,000 feet of sediments to accumulate. The sinking was then interrupted by the uplift that formed the Black Hills. In eastern Wyoming, the blanket of shallow marine sediments was re-elevated and tipped toward the west, and its upturned edge subsequently eroded into a long strip of badlands, averaging a mile or two in width. By then an enormous amount of time had elapsed since the sediments were originally formed.

The fossils of many kinds of marine organisms may be found weathering out of the surface of the badlands. Among them are the shells of extinct squid-like creatures, which have been named *Baculites*. Their bodies were contained within a chamber in the front end of a long cylindrical shell. The shell tapers to the rear and finally terminates in a tiny snail-like coil. The living animals, measuring up to several feet in length, were probably free-floating, although they may have been able to move rapidly

Restoration of a living baculite, and some of the baculite shells found in marine sediments throughout the western interior of North America. Number 1, Baculites obtusus, *is the lowest (oldest) form known from the Black Hills, and the other numbers refer to forms occurring higher (later) in the sequence. Number 15 is* Baculites cuneatus *and number 20 is* Baculites grandis.

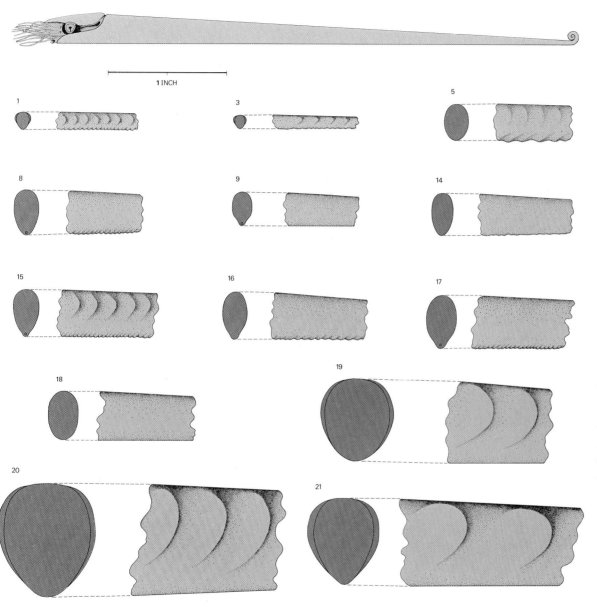

1 INCH

1

3

5

8

9

14

15

16

17

18

19

20

21

over short distances with the aid of a jet of water expelled from a special sac within the body.

Baculite shells from near the bottom of the mudstone blanket are relatively small, bearing coarse ridges on the side and fine ridges along the bottom. As shells are collected from successively higher levels in the overlying 2,400 feet of sediments, they become larger, the sides become smooth, then ribbed, only to become smooth, ribbed, and smooth again. Their bottoms bear fine, coarse, fine, coarse, and, ultimately, fine ridges. In the upper 650 feet of marine sediments, a new and larger kind of baculite shell is found, which in turn becomes larger and then smaller, and the ridges on its side become more widely spaced as the top of the mudstone blanket is approached. Shells from near the bottom of the sedimentary sequence were buried first and are older, and shells from near the top were buried later and are less ancient. The baculite shells were therefore changing with the gradual passage of time and accumulation of sediments.

The blanket of marine sediments on the western slope of the Black Hills can be separated into 21 intergrading "sub-blankets" on the basis of the shapes of the fossil *Baculites* they contain. Two hundred and fifty miles to the south, along the Colorado Front Range, exposures of another series of marine sediments, 5,000 feet thick, contain the same 21 types of fossil shells in the same sequence. Throughout the great trough, wherever a fossil shell of one of these 21 particular types is found, it is assumed that the sediments it was buried in accumulated at the same time as did sediments in other areas that contain similar shells. A shell type, then, can be taken to represent a period of time during which the animals carrying them were living and, upon dying, could contribute their vacant shells to sediments slowly accumulating on the floor of the sea.

We know that the shell shapes of these ancient squid-like creatures reflect the passage of time, and that they can be used to identify the relative ages of sedimentary layers many hundreds or even thousands of miles apart. Yet how many years ago did these animals live, and for how many years did shells of one type endure before they were slowly replaced by shells of another type?

Long ago a delta was flooded by the sea near the site of the city of Lethbridge, in southern Alberta. If we carefully search the exposures

of marine mudstones immediately overlying the deltaic sands, silts and coals, we will find the nearly smooth shells of a species of baculite known as *Baculites cuneatus.* During the time when these shells were being buried on the sea floor, a large volcanic eruption occurred some 200 miles to the south. Volcanic ash falling into the sea formed a layer of ash on the sea floor within the sediments containing the *Baculites cuneatus* shells. The ash fall contained minute amounts of radioactive potassium in a mineral called sanidine. At the rate of 472 atoms per million million atoms of radioactive potassium per year, the potassium has been changing to argon, a rare gas. By carefully measuring the amount of radioactive potassium left in the tiny sanidine crystals and the amount of argon that has been produced, and comparing these quantities to the amount of argon produced during one year, the time that has elapsed since the ash was blown from the volcano can be calculated. By this means it is known that the ash near

Lethbridge is approximately 73 million years old, and that the ancient delta was already flooded at that time.

Baculites cuneatus shells have also been found in the valley of the South Saskatchewan River in Saskatchewan, near the Black Hills in Wyoming, and along the Front Ranges of Colorado. Because the animals that could produce this kind of shell must have lived during one general interval of time, it follows that these areas were also under the sea about 73 million years ago. *Baculites cuneatus* shells constitute the fifteenth consecutive shell type to be found above the base of the marine mudstones near the Black Hills. The twentieth shell type in the sequence, named *Baculites grandis,* is very large and bears heavy ridges on each side. In Montana, volcanic ash that fell to the sea floor during *Baculites grandis* time is about 70 million years old. Many other sequences of shell types, apart from the 21 forms discovered near the Black Hills, have been identified in sediments that were deposited near the end of the dinosaurian era. Several other volcanic-ash falls have also been dated. It would appear from these dates that the time span represented by a particular shell type amounts to an average of about 500,000 years. Using the information from the ash falls and shell types, the ages of sediments deposited throughout the great trough during the last part of the dinosaurian era can be estimated.

Regions where Baculites cuneatus *shells have been collected in marine mudstones. Pale-blue areas to the north indicate the flooded delta; light-brown areas to the south indicate land that emerged as the northern delta was flooded.*

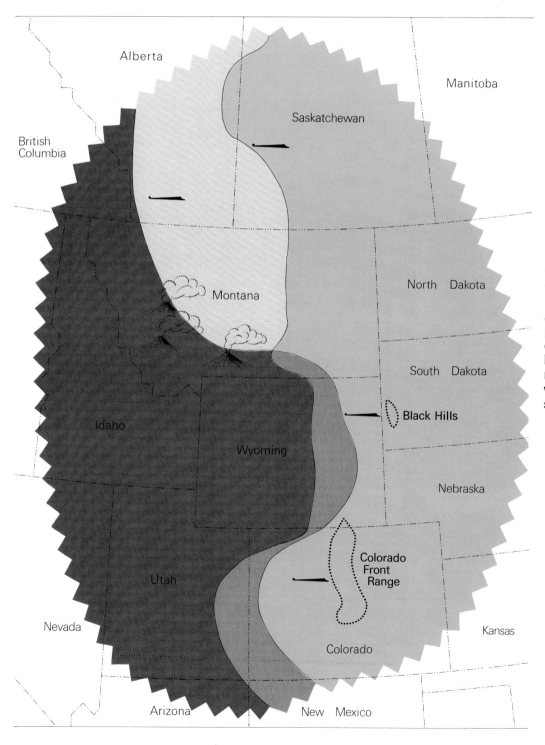

The Geography of a Vanished World

Knowing the ages of these sediments, an earth scientist can begin to visualize North America as it may have been at various points in time, and can thus become acquainted with its history. Indeed, with the aid of the fossil remains of organisms, which slowly changed with the passing millenia, and the radioactive elements in mineral crystals, which gradually decompose at known rates, the history of our earth is now being deciphered. The means by which sediments of a given age can be identified are available. Let us select a level in time of about 80 million years before the present and see what can be deduced from the sediments about the character of the northern part of our continent. First, evidence relating to topography will be examined, and then that which relates to climate. We will find that we possess a much better impression of the geography of our part

29

of the planet when the dinosaurs were alive than did Cartier of the new lands beyond the western horizon when he left Saint Malo in 1534 to explore them for Francis I.

A review of the series of baculite forms and the ages during which they are estimated to have lived shows that the shells of *Baculites obtusus* are indicators of a time about 80 million years ago. These shells bear coarsely ribbed sides and a serrated bottom, and occur within the lowermost, thus the oldest, mudstones exposed near the Black Hills. They have also been found within similar mudstones throughout Colorado, Wyoming, Montana, and southern Alberta. Marine mudstones of this age are exposed on the surface of the ground or have been penetrated by wells throughout most of the Prairie Provinces. To the west, the mudstones pass into fossil beach-sands, then into deltaic silts and swamp deposits near the Alberta–British Columbia border. East of the Pembina Mountains, in south-central Manitoba, sediments of this age have been removed by erosion. At the easternmost limit of their present distribution, however, they still

resemble sediments that were deposited on a sea floor many miles away from land. The shore must have lain much farther east, in western Ontario. Eighty million years ago, then, the mid continent was covered by an interior sea, which was at least a thousand miles wide at the present boundary between Canada and the United States.

If Cartier could have traversed 80 million years of time as well as the breadth of the Atlantic Ocean, our charts suggest that he would have been diverted to the northwest into a shallow, narrow channel flanked for hundreds of miles by steep cliffs. If this strait was navigable, *la Grande Hermine* could have sailed to the southwest through a broad gulf in the region of Hudson Bay. To the north lay a large island of ancient crystalline rocks, from which rivers flowed to the arctic sea. To the south lay the island continent of Appalachia, with chains of rounded ranges bordering its southeastern coast. The gulf then opened toward the west into

a vast interior sea that extended across what was to become the prairies, from the Arctic Ocean to the Gulf of Mexico. However, even then, Cartier would have found his way to the riches of Cathay blocked by a great chain of mountains rising out of the sea to the west.

We have noted that the western mountains were very unstable. The continent of North America had long ago begun to separate from Europe and Africa, and these mountains marked a vast zone of disturbance where continental rocks were being pushed over the relatively heavier rocks of the Pacific floor. Earthquakes occurred frequently in this region as volcanoes were formed and great masses of molten granitic rock invaded the roots of mountain ranges. The magnetic field of the earth acted on the crystals of iron minerals in the cooling molten masses just as it now directs the ends of a compass needle toward the North and South poles, and they were frozen in that position in the cooling rock. The iron minerals suspended in sediments were similarly oriented before the sediments were compressed into stone. The age of the once-molten granite can be measured by the amount of radioactive potassium in its minerals that has changed into argon, and the age of the sediments can be measured by the baculite shells and ash falls within them.

*A map of Canada as it was 80
million years ago*

▲ North Pole

Arctic

Circle

50° N

Thus, iron minerals in granitic and sedimentary rocks exposed in the Arctic islands, Quebec and California, all of which are about 100 million years old, were "fossilized" pointing to the north magnetic pole of that time. The northward-pointing lines all converge on a pole located due west of Alaska, which was moving very slowly toward its present location in the centre of the Arctic Ocean.

By 80 million years ago, when *Baculites obtusus* was alive, the North Pole had arrived at a point about 200 miles off the northwest coast of Alaska. If the earth's axis of rotation was inclined about 23° to the plane of its orbit around the sun, as it is today, the Arctic Circle would have crossed Canada from the Queen Charlotte Islands off the coast of British Columbia in the west, through Great Slave Lake in the District of Mackenzie, to Ellesmere Island off the northwest coast of Greenland in the east. Relative to the position of the Pole, Vancouver would have been about 600 miles farther north 80 million years ago, and the St. Lawrence valley would have been about 600 miles farther south. Accordingly, the ancient Rocky Mountains and the western shore of the interior sea were then oriented in a north-south direction.

Plant remains have been recovered from the deltaic deposits that lined the flanks of the ancient Rockies between 80 million and 60 million years ago. The fossil trunks, leaves and pollen indicate climatic conditions different from those prevailing in these regions today. For example, among the living broad-leaved trees, it is known that those bearing smooth-margined leaves, such as cucumber trees, tulip poplars and paw-paws, are more commonly found in warmer regions. Conversely, trees with leaves having serrate margins, such as mountain ash, birch and trembling aspen, are more typical of cooler regions. About 10 per cent of the broad-leaved trees living in Alberta today have leaves with smooth margins, while 41 per cent of those living in Louisiana bear smooth-margined leaves. Among British Columbia trees represented by leaf fossils that are about 70 million years old, some 50 per cent had leaves with smooth margins.

If sufficient water is available, a warmer climate will support a greater variety of plants than a cooler one. Thus members of only 11 families of plants attain tree size in Alberta, while representatives of 42 families attain tree size in Louisiana, which is much smaller in area. About 70 million years ago, at least 51 plant families containing species of tree size were present in or near southern Alberta. It is therefore apparent that, at that time, southern British Columbia, Alberta and Saskatchewan enjoyed climates at least as warm as those prevailing today along the northern coast of the Gulf of Mexico. This is further reflected in the presence of fossil cycad, palm, breadfruit, and cinnamon leaves in sediments of this general age in southwestern Canada.

To the north, deltas were forming along the eastern margin of the ancient Rocky Mountain land-mass far beyond the Arctic Circle of that time, nearly to the North Pole off the present northwest coast of Alaska. In the vicinity of Great Bear Lake and northern Yukon Territory, these deposits have yielded fossil pollen of bald cypress, which grows today along the southern Atlantic and Gulf coasts, as well as that of cycads, subtropical conifers, and tree ferns. On the north slope of Alaska, some 400 miles from the ancient North Pole, grew ginkgoes, redwoods and sycamores. Mild climates evidently extended as far as the Pole, where temperatures were similar to those of northern California today. However, because of the inclination of the earth's axis of rotation, the Arctic, then as now, was a land of the midnight sun and continuous, if relatively balmy, winter darkness. Plant growth must have been vigorous during the summer, but probably ceased during the long dark season, when plants would have had to remain dormant in order to survive.

Our sixteenth-century navigators would have found a strange world indeed if they had reached North America as it was 80 million years ago. Warm, shallow seas would have enabled their wooden ships to follow swampy, insect-infested coastlines far into the interior of the continent. Whale-like lizards 30 feet long would have lazily undulated away from their vessels, slipping through waters muddied by seasonal floods from mountains beyond the western horizon. Shrieks and trumpetings from the land by night and the sight of dragon-like creatures basking on estuary banks by day would have convinced the explorers that they had in truth approached "the land God gave to Cain".

The marine lizard Platecarpus *feeding on* Baculites obtusus *near Morden, Manitoba. The large fish in the background, Protosphyraena, are ancient "swordfish" distantly related to the modern bowfins.*

III A Park for Dinosaurs

Silts and sands rich in plant-derived carbonaceous material deposited near stream banks, Oldman Formation, Dinosaur Provincial Park (S72-3975)

Prairie Badlands

The city of Brooks lies on the Trans-Canada Highway near the centre of the southern Alberta prairies. Eight miles to the north and ten miles to the east, via provincial highway 36 and a gravel road, lies the village of Patricia, formerly a station on the Canadian Pacific Railway. Here many tons of fossils were loaded into boxcars and shipped to museums throughout Canada and the United States. Northeast of Patricia the road crosses a shortgrass prairie that has not been disturbed by cultivation and stretches seemingly to the horizon. After a few miles one approaches a large sign, cut in the shape of the province of Alberta and painted with reconstructions of several varieties of dinosaurs, announcing the boundary of Dinosaur Provincial Park. Then the prairie abruptly terminates in a sea of nearly 15,000 acres of broken terrain. Toward the centre of the badlands winds the Red Deer River, bordered by thin groves of cottonwood and aspen. In these beautiful but harsh surroundings, men have arduously laboured to excavate and pack bones from the skeletons of some 300 dinosaurs. Four- and six-horse teams once brought the

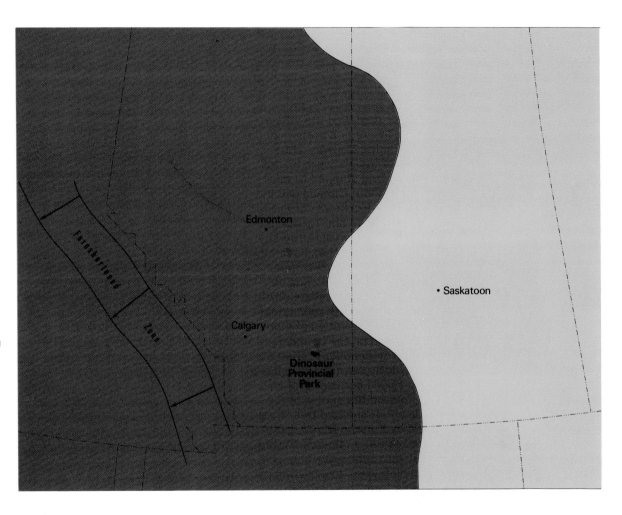

The geography of southern Alberta 76 million years ago, showing the present location of Dinosaur Provincial Park

heavy crates up the road that now leads from the prairie rim to the Park headquarters near the river.

The badlands are a wilderness of fluted and rounded shapes carved into the ancient sands and mudstones by the runoff from summer storms and melting snows. According to the *Baculites* and volcanic-ash time indicators, these sediments were deposited about 76 million years ago, following an elevation of the entire western edge of the Rocky Mountains. The western ranges probably were high and received heavy rains, for the volume of sediments that spread from them indicates the rapid erosion of their sedimentary strata before an abundance of running water. Rivers carried the sediments eastwards across a broad floodplain to deltas bordering the shore of the retreating sea. The ancient alluvial plain has since been shortened about 80 miles by movements within the earth's crust. At that time, however, it extended nearly 300 miles between the mountains and the sea, and was as broad as the coastal plain now bordering the northern coast of the Gulf of Mexico. Seventy-six million years ago,

38

Blue river-sands and orange levees,
Oldman Formation, Dinosaur
Provincial Park (S72-3985)

Rubble of hardened levee deposits
and glacial boulders on river sands,
Oldman Formation, Dinosaur
Provincial Park (S73-631)

the site of Dinosaur Provincial Park was on this flat alluvial plain, about 225 miles east of the Rockies. Some 65 miles to the northeast lay the nearest arm of the sea, a bay between two large deltas, one of which was located in the vicinity of what are today the Cypress Hills in southwestern Saskatchewan and the other to the southeast of Lake Athabasca. The level of the interior sea had fallen, and its eastern shore may not have reached northwestern Ontario. Its width along the Forty-ninth Parallel was reduced to about 500 miles.

Long ago, dinosaurs lived and died within the region that is now Dinosaur Provincial Park. Looking at the barren shapes of the Park under a blazing summer sun or bluish mid-winter snows, it is difficult to comprehend how this could have been so. Dinosaurs could not now find enough food to nourish their massive bodies, nor shelter to protect their naked skins from today's climatic extremes. The ancient world in which they lived has vanished, but traces of its everyday events remain within the sediments from which the rocks were formed: a rapidly flowing stream washed a hollow into its bed of clay, and then filled the hollow with sand; a dead leaf fell into a lake, to be covered with silt; or a decaying fish floated away from a bar, leaving a spine behind imbedded in sand. It is through the record of such events in the rocks that we can understand what the Park was like when the dinosaurs lived there. Let us attempt to read this ancient record, written in letters of tiny particles of stone.

*River sands, Oldman Formation,
Dinosaur Provincial Park (S72-4049)*

From Sediments to Landscapes

Who has not seen snow float to the ground, whence it is swept away by the wind, to be deposited in banks and drifts elsewhere? Currents of water transport and shape bodies of sand and silt at the bottoms of streams in the same way. From the many directions in which inclined layers of sediment slope in the Park, one can deduce that the currents that shaped them meandered widely to the north and south as they flowed eastwards to the sea. Irregular, uneven layering reflects water turbulence. Conversely, broad, flat layers of silt and mud indicate quiet water conditions where flood waters slowed, depositing their sedimentary load in lakes formed from abandoned stream channels and on floodplains near river courses.

Just as the wind must blow in gusts of about 20 miles an hour before it begins to move large quantities of dry snow on the ground, so also is the strength of a current of water revealed by the sedimentary particles it carries. Muds and silts can be transported by relatively slow-moving streams, but cobbles and pebbles can only be moved by torrents. The largest particles carried by the streams that once flowed through the Park are fine grains of sand, measuring from one-eighth to one-quarter of a millimetre in diameter. To have carried particles of this size the currents

River sands with lenticular bodies of mudstone deposited in quieter eddies, Oldman Formation, Dinosaur Provincial Park (S73-619)

Cross-bedded river sands, Oldman Formation, Dinosaur Provincial Park (S73-621)

River sands overlying floodplain deposits, Oldman Formation, Dinosaur Provincial Park (S72-4114)

43

River sands, Oldman Formation,
Dinosaur Provincial Park (S72-3989)

must have flowed at a speed of about half a mile an hour. Because about 70 per cent of the sediments in the Park are fine sands and the remainder silts and clays, it would appear that the sands were more frequently left behind by the currents than were the silts and clays. Currents of about one-quarter of a mile an hour would thus have been typical. Bar deposits in the ancient streams and deltaic accumulations in abandoned channels indicate that the larger streams were at least 15 feet deep.

The sediments in the Park are unusual for the number of times they were redisturbed by streams before they finally came to rest in their present form. Several fossil environments are recognizable in the sediments. An irregular surface, worn into the sedimentary layer below, typically marks the centre of a former channel. At its base, clay pebbles and fossil bones are commonly found buried in a bed of fine sand. Bars within channels or along the banks of streams are

Sediment structures produced by current action within a stream meander

River sands, Oldman Formation, Dinosaur Provincial Park (S73-618)

Channel sands grading upwards into ledge-forming levee deposits, Oldman Formation, Dinosaur Provincial Park (S72-3970)

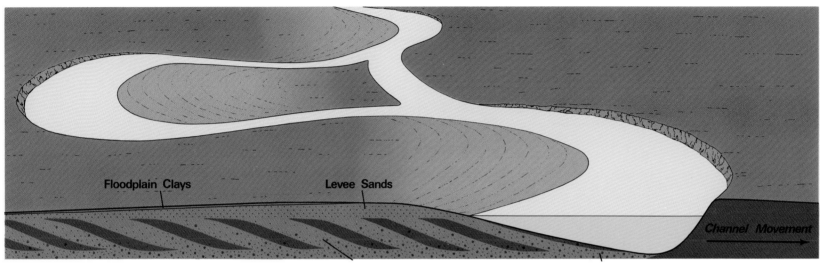

Floodplain Clays

Levee Sands

Channel Movement

Point-Bar Silts and Clays

Channel Sands

Point-bar deposits, Oldman Formation, Dinosaur Provincial Park (S72-3995)

Floodplain deposits rich in volcanic ash, Oldman Formation, Dinosaur Provincial Park (S72-4011)

characterized by alternating sandy and silty layers, in which the lighter bones, drifted logs, and broken, poorly preserved plant material are imbedded. The streams were often lined by narrow, slightly elevated areas called levees, where the coarsest materials were deposited from high, rapidly flowing flood-waters. Because the levees were usually above the level of the water, they contain the fossilized roots of terrestrial plants, as well as hard calcareous or reddish iron-rich concretions formed by water per-colating down from the soil surface to the water table. Beyond the levees, the finer silts and clays were deposited over wide areas during times of high water. These sediments gradually filled the oxbow lakes that were formed when part of a curving channel was cut off as the parent stream found a new course. They were also spread over many square miles of adjacent low-lying floodplain. Because the streams that flowed across the Park meandered so widely to the north and south, they destroyed much of the floodplain deposits, and swept their finer sediments

out to the deltas by the sea. In the course of their meanderings, they also broke many fossil skeletons apart and dispersed the bones widely along their channels. It is for this reason that isolated bones are so frequently found scattered over the exposures of sedimentary rock in the Park.

Bodies of water-drifted sand, similar to those that filled the fossil stream channels and oxbow lakes in the Park, have been traced in oil wells for hundreds of miles to the north and south. During the time when the mountains were being most heavily eroded, many large, meandering streams must have flowed from them across the broad floodplain to the east. These altered their courses frequently, probably during floods, so that the entire plain was covered at one time or another with river-transported sand. The rivers must have been rather broad in relation to their depth, and the many sand bars they contained probably gave them a braided appearance. Because of the winding of their channels, and the presence of cut-off oxbow lakes, the area paralleling a river course must have been almost entirely covered with either standing or slow-moving water. Near the streams, such dry land surfaces as existed were probably sandy, and consisted of the linear or oblong shapes of levees and exposed bars. The silts and clays of the periodically inundated floodplain must have lain several miles away from the main axes of stream flow.

Petrified Vestiges of Life

Several varieties of freshwater clams and snails, which are related to forms that inhabit the larger rivers today, have been found in the Park. The tumbled bones of fishes occur abundantly at the bottoms of fossil stream channels. Among the most common of these are the heavily armoured scales of gars, a fish averaging some three feet in length. The presence of moderately large sturgeons, perhaps six feet long and over 100 pounds in weight, is indicated by fossil fin-spines and body-plates. Another heavy-bodied fish related to the modern bowfin also grew to this size. The stingless ray reached a length of three feet and probably fed on clams and snails. The crushing teeth of these creatures are found in abundance. Falling midway between rays and sharks in body

Bald cypress in stream and hardwood forest on opposite bank of Black Creek northeast of Wiggins, Mississippi (S73-560)

shape, sawfishes bear a row of teeth around the edge of a long, flat snout that resembles the blade of a chain saw. Their teeth are rarely found. Another slender-billed fish with armoured scales could, like the rays, also inhabit brackish and marine waters. The bones of an eight-foot aquatic reptile, belonging to a group of more typically marine creatures called plesiosaurs, are occasionally collected. They possessed flippers and a long snake-like neck, and fed on fishes. Their presence, together with that of the salt-tolerant fishes, suggests that large, open bodies of slow-moving water linked the ancient aquatic environments of the Park with the open sea 65 miles to the northeast.

Fossilized pieces of wood and logs, measuring up to 2 feet in diameter and 52 feet in length, have been found in many areas of the Park. Their petrified woody tissues and the occurrence of isolated fossil cones indicate that the logs belonged to redwood trees. These were probably uprooted and toppled into streams during times of high water, and transported to the Park from the west. Broken and partly decayed vegetation of local origin is abundantly preserved in the

fossil stream and lake deposits, suggesting that plant life flourished in the region. However, most of the material is too fragmentary to be identified, and, with some exceptions, only a few well-preserved stems, branch tips, or leaves of any single variety of plant have been collected. The only pollen and spores from plants living at the time that have been identified so far were taken from the fossilized excrement of a crocodile, although these microscopic grains are surely abundantly present within the silts and clays. Enough is known, however, to convey some impression of the ancient plant life of Dinosaur Provincial Park.

Water lilies grew in the quiet waters of abandoned channels and oxbow lakes. The shallow borders of these bodies of water and surrounding mud flats supported extensive growths of cattails, and their reedy foliage, broken and mixed with layers of sand and silt, is very abundant. The areas of sandy, dry land adjacent to the rivers probably did not escape destruction from stream erosion for long. Consequently, mature forest stands would not have had time to become established, and the trees that could inhabit these environments must have grown rapidly, set fruit and seeds early, and preferred open, well-lighted growing conditions. The delicate fronds of dawn redwoods, which are

Dawn redwood, Arboretum, Central
Experimental Farm, Ottawa
(S75-1383)

Katsura tree, Arboretum, Central Experimental Farm, Ottawa (S75-1385)

Scouring rushes with sycamore saplings in background, Tunica Hills south of Weyanoche, Louisiana (S73-608)

shed annually like the needles of larches, have been preserved in quantity at some localities. These trees can grow at the rate of five to six feet a year, and may have occurred in clumps on the older, upstream portions of stabilized bars.

Sycamore saplings were probably scattered among the narrow, dense growths of six-foot scouring rushes that must have lined the banks of streams. Behind these, higher on the levees, were probably squat breadfruit trees and conical evergreen torreyas. Perhaps the older, abandoned levees supported a variety of more mature trees, such as the larger sycamores and taller torreyas, the latter bearing seeds enclosed within plum-like fruits near the ends of their branches. Thickets of bushy, round-leaved katsura trees may have grown within and around the edges of the open groves, together with an occasional spiny china fir. The treed, hummocky areas were probably draped with vines bearing leaves like those of wild grape or moonseed. Many kinds of lycopods and ferns as well as lily-like forms and arum plants, which are familiar to us as calla-lilies and monstera respectively, inhabited moist ground shaded by the trees.

Sycamore saplings and scouring rushes, Tunica Hills south of Weyanoche, Louisiana (S73-553)

China fir, south of Hattiesburg, Mississippi (S73-582)

Cattail swamp dotted with clumps of bald cypresses, tupelos and other swamp hardwoods, near the north shore of Lake Pontchartrain, Louisiana (S73-612)

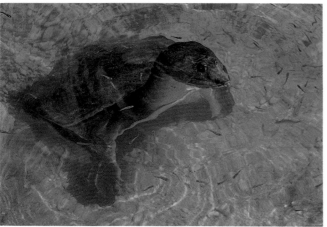

Numerous other varieties of plants, whose appearance is not known, were also present. Some of these were epiphytes, or plants that grow on trees and derive their moisture and nutrients from rain.

If our explorers could have landed on the eastern coast of Alberta 76 million years ago, and taken their longboats 60 miles inland through tidal estuaries and winding, sand-choked rivers to the future site of the Park, they would have seen a landscape very different from the arid prairies and badlands of today. Standing on top of a levee covered with rushes and large-leaved, chest-high saplings, they could have surveyed broad expanses of cattail marshes. Scattered among the reed fields, as hummocks are now scattered through the saw-grass marshes of the Everglades, were clumps and linear groves of trees. The conical shapes of exotic needle-bearing evergreens dominated the outlines of the groves, which were nevertheless often broken by the rounded crowns of one or two giant white-barked sycamores. Where the cattail marshes nearly reached the horizon, the dark line of the distant floodplain forest was visible, separating the fields of reeds and hidden oxbow lakes from the fields of fleecy clouds in the sky.

Turtles could be seen everywhere along the rivers, sunning themselves on exposed sand bars or near drift logs on the shore. At least four major varieties could be distinguished, the adults of which averaged between eight inches and three feet in length. At infrequent intervals, as the boat glided past the banks, an eight-foot-long broad-nosed crocodile would have plunged into the stream, or more rarely a true alligator of about the same size. Beyond the levees and within the lily-pad-covered oxbow lakes, soft-shelled turtles and elongated aquatic salamanders flourished. Six-foot reptiles with long, slender jaws also fed on the small fishes in the quiet waters. These extinct swimming creatures, which have been named champsosaurs, had bodies resembling those of crocodilians. They evidently spent much of their time submerged on the bottoms of the shallow lakes, waiting for their prey to swim over them within reach of their jaws.

Small lizards scurried through the dense vegetation growing near the tops of the stream banks and in the clumps of trees. Beneath them, probing through the decaying foliage for fallen seeds, nuts and fruits, were small squirrel-like mammals. These archaic creatures possessed tiny pouches where they suckled their young, as do kangaroos, but they may have hatched their young from eggs. Primitive opossums the size of small cats fed on carrion, insects and immature reptiles along the water courses. The diminutive mammals, their tiny furred bodies in striking contrast to the smooth, damp surfaces of the world in which they lived, were probably most active during the night. They would then have been protected by the darkness from the attacks of prowling, four-foot-long monitor lizards. Curiously, snakes were either rare or altogether absent. High over the oxbow lakes and marshes, an occasional bat-winged flying reptile circled. The remains of flying reptiles are rarely found, and so far only a single fragment of a bone, from near the base of the finger supporting the wing, has been collected in the Park. The proportions of the fragment indicate that the skeleton must have had a wingspan of about eleven feet.

The presence of these varieties of plant and animal life indicate that the climate was warm and without extremes of temperature. Crocodiles, torreyas, china firs, and breadfruit trees do not occur in regions subjected to seasonal frosts. That the humidity was generally high is suggested by the presence of plants that grow on trees, the probable extent of open water surfaces, the abundance of aquatic organisms preserved in the sediments, and even the sombre colour of the sediments themselves. The annual climate, however, probably alternated between wetter and drier periods. This is reflected in the growth rings preserved in the fossil wood and in the bones of champsosaurs. During the rainier season the waters rose, carrying floating logs with them, depositing a layer of sand on the bars along the edges of the streams, and spreading a layer of silt far beyond the immediate vicinity of the channels. The water levels fell during the drier season, and layers of silt and mud coated the formerly sandy surfaces of the stream-side bars. Flecks of charcoal scattered through the channel sands indicate that the region could become dry enough to support burns.

Small, rounded drops of fossil resin, or amber, occur within sediments that also contain an abundance of carbonized plant material. Seventy-six million years ago this sticky substance oozed from the wounds of conifers. Insects were trapped within it and are preserved in astonishing detail. Thus, it is known that web-spinning spiders were present in the Park at that time, together with sap-sucking insects and beetles. Ants and termites burrowed in dry, sandy areas, and built aerial nests or mounds on the floors of wooded areas. Most trying to the crew of explorers, who would have had to haul and row their longboats down many miles of humid inland rivers, would have been clouds of tiny biting flies, or "no-see-ums".

Reptilian Giants
The creatures that would have made the greatest impression on the explorers have never been seen by man. These are the members of the two general kinds of extinct reptiles known to us as dinosaurs. The remains of some 25 varieties of dinosaurs have been excavated from the sediments that filled the ancient water courses and oxbow lakes of Dinosaur Provincial Park. The carcasses of the larger animals that had either died in stream channels or whose bodies had been carried there were usually buried in sand and lay approximately parallel to the water flow, in an east-westward direction. These were often dismembered by the currents. The carcasses that came to rest away from the main channels in slower-moving water or in oxbow lakes are frequently oriented in a north-southward direction, perhaps blown

to this position by the prevailing winds from the west. These skeletons were buried in finer sand and silt, and were usually less disturbed by currents. The remains of the smaller dinosaurs, whose isolated bones and teeth are frequently preserved, are very rarely found as entire skeletons. Their more delicate skeletal elements could evidently be dispersed by even slow-moving water. Large numbers of skeletons of all sizes were destroyed as the rivers changed their courses and eroded through previously deposited sediments. The bones were scattered downstream, and occasionally were swept together into subaqueous drifts, or "bone-beds", on the bottoms of the stream courses. Dinosaur remains are infrequently preserved in the fine-grained silts and clays of the floodplain, where they were often destroyed by scavengers or disintegrated through decay.

The dinosaurs that formerly inhabited the region of the Park can be separated into two groups based on size. At least ten varieties of dinosaurs, most of them imperfectly known, were relatively small, apparently having weighed between 100 and 200 pounds. By way of comparison, the 8-foot crocodiles that inhabited the water courses of that time were probably about as heavy as the smaller dinosaurs. A second group of at least fifteen varieties of dinosaurs ranged from 12 to 26 feet long, and probably weighed between three and four tons. The largest crocodilians living today attain lengths of 23 feet and weights of slightly over a ton. The heavier land mammals occurring in Canada today, such as the bison, polar bear, moose, and elk, range between one-half to slightly more than one ton in weight. A four-ton dinosaur would have seemed quite ponderous beside modern large Canadian mammals.

However, the great mammals of the African and Asian tropics attain weights equal to and exceeding those estimated for these dinosaurs. Rhinos may weigh as much as a ton and a half, hippopotami three tons, and large bull elephants up to six tons. The larger dinosaurs found in the Park would not have seemed extraordinarily massive in relation to some of these familiar living mammals, although the variety of large reptiles there would have seemed unusual. Giant dinosaurs did inhabit equatorial regions of the earth at that time. Nevertheless, the apparent size of a half-ton grizzly 20 feet away in an animal enclosure is very different from that of a similar animal at the same distance in the Barren Grounds of the North. The dinosaurs of the Park would have appeared adequately large!

It would probably be unwise to project similarities between dinosaurs and large mammals beyond the general attribute of size. The dinosaurs were reptiles. At least some of them possessed naked skins and relatively simple brains, and they laid eggs. Whether or not dinosaurs could maintain their body temperature at a constant level, as do mammals and birds, is uncertain. The bulk of the larger varieties was nevertheless sufficient to reduce the effect of temperature changes of 4° to 8° C between the hot days and cooler nights of their subtropical environment. It has been suggested that some dinosaurs, such as the horned dinosaurs, could run or gallop in the manner of hoofed mammals. The relatively imperfect limb joints, the heaviness of the feet, and the lack of special structures to support the often massive head imply that this was not true. The gaits of large tortoises, crocodiles or monitor lizards must convey some notion of normal dinosaurian movement, although the walking or ambling movements of large mammals are probably also similar, if more supple. Some dinosaurs were apparently capable of long seasonal migrations.

All dinosaurs, whether they fed on animals or plants, depended heavily on sight to locate their food. Presumably they were most active during the day, and, like many other reptiles and birds, were probably colour-seeing animals. Many mammals, particularly carnivores such as wolves and lions, are partially or completely colour-blind.

Dinosaurian predators and their prey alike must have been colour-camouflaged, and more difficult for us to see than, for example, a brown deer against a background of green summer foliage.

Although dinosaur eggs have been collected in abundance in other countries, such as Mongolia, China and France, it is curious that no shell fragments have yet been reported from Dinosaur Provincial Park. Perhaps in the future someone will discover why this is so, although shell fragments of dinosaur eggs have been found in sediments of the same age in Montana. The bones of young dinosaurs are rare, and are almost never found in a complete skeleton. This may have been a consequence of their small size, their remains having been devoured, or scattered by the currents. Perhaps the life span of dinosaurs, like that of many reptiles, was longer than that of mammals of similar body size, and fewer young animals were needed to sustain adult populations. Perhaps, also, the open environments, broken by numerous bodies of water, did not provide adequate shelter to protect younger animals from the attacks of carnivores.

The skeletal remains of the helmeted duckbilled dinosaur *Corythosaurus* were buried in abundance along the fossil stream courses of Dinosaur Provincial Park. This creature is known to virtually every schoolchild interested in dinosaurs, and indeed is as representative of the dinosaurs of Canada as is any form. Its body was graceful, with a highly flexible goose-like neck, a narrow, arched back, and a deep, narrow tail. The hind limbs were large and powerfully constructed, but the slender, possibly webbed, forelimbs were better suited as balancing aids than for support. The head was duck-like, although a hollow crest covered the skull behind the beak. Within this crest, the narial passageways arched over the head to come together and descend in front of the eyes into the throat. As the carcasses of many of these specimens came to rest, the fine-grained sands and silts filled the tiny grooves and bumps on the surface of the skin. The skin then decayed, leaving an impression and carbon film behind in the sediments. These impressions indicate that the skin of *Corythosaurus* was covered with small polygonal tubercles. Rows of larger oval tubercles covered the belly in the pelvic region. A smooth ridge extended along the centre of the back to the tail, and irregular vertical folds of skin descended across the chest in front of the belly.

At one site, four subadult animals with incompletely formed narial crests were excavated, suggesting that the animals may have herded during this stage of their development. Adults grew to lengths of 26 feet and weights of slightly more than 4 tons. Groups of these animals probably followed river courses, walking on sand bars in shallow, cross-channelled regions of the rivers and simply wading or swimming across deeper areas. They probably ate ferns and stripped freshly grown leaves and shoots from young trees and the lower branches of older trees along the stream banks. Perhaps the colour pattern of their bodies was broken at mid height, displaying pale-blue or orange bellies to blend with the sand below, and vertical stripes of browns, greens and light greens above to harmonize with the reed fields around them. Although the purpose of the hollow crest on their heads is a subject of current controversy, some suggest that it served as a resonating chamber in the production of characteristic trumpeting sounds. If this was so, the amount of noise generated by one of these creatures, not to mention a herd of them, when alarmed by a carnivore or during the mating season at the onset of the drier period in the yearly cycle, must have been spectacular.

Less common than *Corythosaurus,* but nevertheless an animal typical of river-bank environments, was the quadrupedal horned dinosaur *Chasmosaurus*. These animals resembled rhinos in size, weight, and even, to some extent, general

A carcass of the horned dinosaur
Chasmosaurus *in a stream channel*
during the dry season. The small
scavenger is Dromaeosaurus.
Dinosaur Provincial Park, northeast
of Brooks, Alberta.

appearance. They differed most obviously from rhinos in possessing a horny beak, bony shield at the back of the head, short forelimbs held out from, rather than beneath, the body, and a longer, heavier tail. The neck shield and nose and brow horns were obviously used in self-defence. The animal confronted its opponent by pivoting about on its hind limbs, and thrusting its horns forwards and upwards with its powerful front limbs and neck. Its beak would also have been a formidable defensive weapon. The skin has been preserved over the pelvic region of one specimen, whose small polygonal tubercles are much larger than in *Corythosaurus*. In the horned dinosaur, the larger tubercles extend over the back to nearly the midline of the body, and are sizable, measuring over 2 inches in diameter. Both large and small tubercles decrease in size toward the belly.

The teeth are placed close together in elongated magazines near the back of the jaws, and, instead of bearing somewhat elephant-like grinding surfaces similar to those of *Corythosaurus*, the biting surfaces are vertical, indicating that *Chasmosaurus* sliced rather than chewed its food. The leverage and strength of the muscles that closed its jaws were such that the animal, and indeed all horned dinosaurs, must have had an extremely powerful bite. *Chasmosaurus* evidently required large

quantities of vegetation growing close to the ground, which it cropped with its beak and chopped at the back of its mouth. Perhaps more so than the corythosaurs, chasmosaurs preferred to browse among the reeds and cattails, consuming the shallow, fibrous tubers of these plants.

Isolated bones show that at least five varieties of small flesh-eating dinosaurs frequented the river banks to feed on carrion or to prey upon the smaller animals there. None of these dinosaurs could have weighed much more than 100 pounds, and skeletal material of only two of them is well enough known to permit reconstruction of the habits of these creatures. One of these was *Dromaeosaurus*, a vicious little reptile with a skull about eight inches long armed with curved, finely serrated teeth. The animal was bipedal, but possessed an enlarged eagle-like claw at least three inches long on its inner toe, which it probably used to disembowel its prey. The outer two toes ended in elongated hoofs, upon which the animal ran when the inner toe was flexed. *Stenonychosaurus*, another small carnivorous dinosaur, was generally similar to *Dromaeosaurus*, but the claw on the inner toe was smaller and the animal was possibly more fleet.

Its arms were capable of very precise, coordinated movements. The animal had enormous eyes and an enlarged brain, which indicates that it was capable of behaviour patterns as complicated as those of birds. It had a bill-like muzzle lined with small serrated teeth, and probably fed on lizards and mammals, particularly at twilight. The small size of these two carnivores would have made them vulnerable to chilling during the cooler hours of the night and early morning. They were very active creatures, however, and may have been incipiently warm-blooded, as are some of the lower mammals today. It would be fascinating to know if they had developed an insulating body-cover, analogous to feathers, to protect them from the daily temperature changes of their environment.

The flat, marshy lands bordering the rivers were broken into a patchwork of reed fields, oxbow lakes, stream meanders, and groves of trees growing on abandoned levees. The remains of large flesh-eating dinosaurs are found in the sediments of these regions in unusual abundance, and the environment seems to have been particularly well suited for carnivores. Lying hidden at the edges of clumps of trees, they could seize animals that ventured too near, or trap them within the variable terrain. Game trails along the major streams could easily be surveyed from the nearby borderlands. The most abundant of the large carnivorous dinosaurs was *Albertosaurus* (often incorrectly called *Gorgosaurus*), which like all tyrannosaurs was bipedal. The hind limbs were long and powerful, and the animals were probably the fleetest of the large dinosaurs inhabiting the Park at that time. Although they grew over 25 feet long and weighed several tons, their two-fingered forelimbs were not much larger than those of a man, and were frequently damaged in life, probably crushed by movements of the massive body. The chest and abdomen were protected from the thrusts of horned dinosaurs by a flexible shield of rib-like bones beneath the skin. A bulldog neck ended in a large but lightly constructed skull. *Albertosaurus* clamped its jaws on its prey, deepening the wound and tearing the body of the victim by jerks of the neck, using the inertia of its own body and pushing with its legs. The tyrannosaur simply bolted the soft parts and lighter bony structures of its prey, probably leaving behind for scavengers a large amount of flesh attached to the heavier bones, scattered entrails, and pools of blood. The infant tyrannosaurs had relatively longer limbs than the adults, enabling them to capture smaller, more agile prey and to escape larger predators.

The helmeted duckbill *Corythosaurus* also frequented the marshlands bordering the rivers, but another crested duckbill, *Lambeosaurus,* was at least as abundant there. The cranial hood of this form sloped forward, and often ended behind in a bony boss or rod. Its skin apparently lacked the larger oval tubercles present on the skin of *Corythosaurus,* but the animal was otherwise very similar. The horned dinosaur *Chasmosaurus* appears to have been as abundant here as either of the duckbills.

Solitary armoured dinosaurs of the *Panoplosaurus* variety were also present in both river-course and marshland environments. These massive animals probably weighed between three and four tons, and bore heavy spines along the sides of their squat bodies. Lacking tail clubs, they relied on their strength and armour for defence, perhaps driving the spines along their flanks into the body of an attacking predator and attempting to topple it in a short charge. Their cheeks were protected by bony plates, and their eyes were directed downwards under heavy ridges of bone. The throat was shielded by a blanket of small rounded bones imbedded in the skin, so that the head was well protected against the bite of a tyrannosaur. With their horny, square beaks they cropped and crushed plant material, which they further chopped, to some extent, with their relatively weak teeth. It is difficult to imagine the creatures feeding on anything except delicate or pulpy objects near the surface of the ground. Perhaps they browsed on ferns, lilies and arum plants growing in shaded areas, or pulled cattail tubers from the moist soils of the marshes. That the remains of these animals are infrequently encountered may be because their numbers were controlled by a relatively thin growth of suitable fodder, rather than because they were vulnerable to the attacks of large carnivores.

The preferred habitat of another kind of horned dinosaur, *Centrosaurus,* is more difficult to ascertain. It was about as large as *Chasmosaurus,* but of lankier proportions, with a longer body and limbs. The neck shield was shorter than in *Chasmosaurus,* and more rounded, often bearing a pair of spines that curved forwards near the centre of the rim. The nasal horn is much larger in *Centrosaurus,* and may be either recurved or straight, measuring up to 18 inches in length. It would seem that *Centrosaurus* might have preferred more open environments than *Chasmosaurus.* Nevertheless, its remains are usually found in stream channels, buried in sandstones that were deposited in the faster-flowing parts of streams. Isolated skulls are most frequently found, although entire skeletons have been collected. Perhaps the animals were drowned as they attempted to ford rivers during seasonal north–south migrations.

Remains of armoured dinosaurs of the *Euoplocephalus* variety tend to be preserved in the same manner as those of *Centrosaurus.* Tail clubs still attached by powerful ossified tendons to the end of the tail are found isolated in channel sands, but skeletons are more rare and have usually been scattered. These animals were covered with a coat of bony plates, which typically were not as spiny as those of the pano-plosaurs. Nevertheless, the animals were so completely encased in armour that even their eyelids had large, curved, bony plates. That closely related armoured dinosaurs have been collected from arid in-land deposits in central Asia suggests that *Euoplocephalus* may have drowned in streams in more-inland environments near the Rockies and been carried down-stream to be buried at the future site of the Park.

Many other varieties of dino-saurs have been discovered in Dinosaur Provincial Park, but not as abundantly as the forms already mentioned. The heavy-bodied tyran-nosaur *Daspletosaurus* inhabited marshlands adjacent to the stream courses, as did the strange, small, bone-headed dinosaurs, or pachy-cephalosaurs. The water-worn skull-caps of the latter have been found in abundance in the channel sand-

stones of the Park. Skeletons that are infrequently found include those of other duckbilled dinosaurs, such as the spade-crested *Brachylo-phosaurus*, spike-crested *Prosauro-lophus,* tube-crested *Parasaurolo-phus,* and arched-nosed *Kritosaurus;* horned dinosaurs, such as the spine-frilled *Styracosaurus;* and ostrich dinosaurs. As their remains are nearly always found in channel deposits, these animals may have migrated through the region seasonally, or the carcasses may have lodged there after drifting down from upstream environments.

A Matter of Survival

How could you live in Dinosaur Provincial Park as it was 76 million years ago?

The probability of surviving for any length of time would not be very great. If you must go, dress in a long-sleeved shirt and trousers, and wear a mosquito net around your hat, for biting insects will be abundant. Put a knife, machete, cord, light raincoat, hammock, and mosquito netting in your knapsack, as well as mosquito repellent and matches. These conveniences will help you in the beginning — enabling you to become familiar with your surroundings and in-creasing your chances of long-term survival. So will a high-powered rifle and several hundred rounds of ammunition.

If you are fortunate you will arrive on a wooded, stationary sand bar near the middle of a broad stream. If not, make your way to the nearest clump of trees where herbivorous dinosaurs are grazing quietly and undisturbed, indicating that there may be no tyrannosaurs in the immediate area. Promptly climb a tall open-branched tree where you can hang your hammock at least 25 feet above the ground. The most dangerous animals for you are the tyrannosaurs, both half-grown and adult, and you must learn their habits as soon as possible. These animals are agile and swift, not the ponderous giants pictured in children's books, and your only realistic hope of escape, once seen, is to climb high in the branches of a tree. They depend on their keen vision to locate their prey, and may be least active at night, particularly during the cool pre-dawn hours. It would almost certainly be futile to attempt to shoot a tyrannosaur, particularly in the course of an attack. Their brains are very small and are well protected by bone. If the animal were hit in almost any other part of its body, it would not be diverted,

The tyrannosaur Daspletosaurus *and a fleeing* Champsosaurus *near the edge of a braided stream-course. To the right are dawn redwoods, with katsura trees and china firs in the background. Dinosaur Provincial Park, northeast of Brooks, Alberta.*

even if mortally wounded. Smaller, man-sized carnivorous dinosaurs, such as the dromaeosaurs, would also be extremely dangerous, but here there would be some chance for self-defence with the use of the rifle or, at close quarters, a bark shield and machete. Their claws are their most formidable weapons of attack.

When you have examined your immediate surroundings and are thoroughly satisfied that there are no carnivorous dinosaurs nearby, you may descend and explore the area for food. Do not touch plants that have waxen compound leaves like those of poison ivy, for members of this plant family will certainly be present. You may find breadfruit or edible nuts. A more reliable source of food, however, will be turtles and turtle eggs. You may be able to spear sturgeons, but watch for the crocodilians, which, though not exceptionally large, may be bold. The different kinds of dinosaurs that lived in the region of the Park, and the environments in which they might be found, have already been described. Observe their habits and in what way they might be dangerous to you.

If you can kill an ostrich dinosaur outright, by shooting it in the head or heart so that its body can be recovered without undue risk, you might find their broiled flesh to be excellent. Although wild mushrooms will be plentiful in the woods, it would be best not to eat your ostrich-dinosaur steak with mushroom gravy. These fungi must be identified precisely in order to separate edible and poisonous kinds, and it is not certain that many modern varieties will be present. The small, relatively intelligent *Stenonychosaurus* might possibly be domesticated if raised from a hatchling. Of all the creatures present it is the only one that could, to any degree, fill the role of a dog.

Ultimately, you will have to decide whether or not your chances of avoiding tyrannosaurs for long are very great. You would probably be safest in the high, cool mountains to the west, but if you find your situation in the Park precarious, the probability that you could survive a 200-mile trek across open terrain would be small indeed. It would therefore be better to construct a raft of small trees and float 60 miles downstream to the cypress swamps near the coast. There you could live within the double protection of the water and the trees, relying on fish for food.

IV Environments on an Ancient Delta

River sands of the Oldman Formation grading upwards into marine muds of the Bearpaw Formation near Irvine, Alberta (S72-4012)

The Cliffs of Drumheller

The sands of Dinosaur Provincial Park, and the debris of the ancient world they contained sank beneath the western edge of the interior sea 73 million years ago. The large rivers that once spread sediments across the plains and into the delta in the region where the Cypress Hills now stand had been diverted to other regions by ponderous vertical movements within the western mountains. The floor of the great trough east of the mountains nevertheless continued to sink at a rate of about one inch every 500 years. A shallow sea then spread over southern Alberta, whose western shore extended from southeastern British Columbia to just west of Calgary and Red Deer, and around another delta centred near Fort McMurray in the northeast. For about 2 million years, according to the baculite and volcanic-ash time-indicators, the sea covered southern Alberta, blanketing the region with a layer of brownish-grey mudstone over 500 feet thick. These soft but cohesive sediments resist erosion, and are not sculptured into badlands as readily as are the coarser sediments deposited on land. However, some exposures of the marine mudstones can be seen on top of the river sands of Dinosaur Provincial Park, and along the Bow and St. Mary rivers to the south.

The northern delta continued to be fed by a large river system flowing eastwards from intermontane basins in British Columbia.

*Marine muds of the Bearpaw
Formation grading upwards into
light river sands weathered into
hoodoos in the Horseshoe Canyon
Formation near Willow Creek on
the Red Deer River, Alberta
(S72-4004)*

The quantity of sediment carried to the delta compensated for the gradual sinking of the western margin of the great trough, so that the delta did not fall below sea level. As the sea spread over southern Alberta, vast swamps developed within the northern delta. The coals that formed through the accumulation of peaty plant-material within the swamps have been traced in oil wells for over 80 miles. Between 71 and 72 million years ago, the delta channels began to flow southeastwards, spreading sediments into the Drumheller region. Ten miles below Drumheller on the Red Deer River, the transition from shallow marine to deltaic deposits can be seen within the narrow valley.

Near the bottom of the valley walls, where Willow Creek meets the Red Deer, the brownish-grey mudstones contain the burrows of marine worms and fragments of the shells of marine organisms. These mudstones become more silty as one ascends the valley walls, and then are abruptly overlaid by a 40-foot layer of white sandstone. The sandstone was deposited where a large, meandering river once flowed into the sea. Some of its layers are more resistant to erosion than the bulk of the sand body. They are often weathered into bizarre mushroom-like caps supported by slender columns of softer sediment, which are known in the West as "hoodoos". As the channel of the ancient river moved away from the area through erosion, the drainage from adjacent regions was impaired by its elevated banks, or levees. A backswamp formed in

*Hoodoo in basal river sands of
Horseshoe Canyon Formation, near
Willow Creek on the Red Deer
River, Alberta (S72-4147)*

*Hoodoos in river sands of the
Horseshoe Canyon Formation near
Willow Creek on the Red Deer
River, Alberta (S72-3968)*

Effect of delta stream-channel movement and the sinking of the great trough on the distribution of different kinds of sediments.
Time B is younger than time A, but older than time C; the stream has continued to progress to the right while the adjacent region subsided.

Time D represents an exposure of these sediments as they now appear in the valley walls of the Red Deer River. Beach sands and marine mudstones are absent in more-inland environments.

which peat accumulated. After the departure of the river the drainage improved somewhat, but once again there was an inadequate supply of sediments to compensate for the gradual sinking of the great trough in this region. A broad 20-foot layer of beach sands was swept in by longshore and tidal currents, bringing the area up to sea level. A coastal swamp developed and, with it, another layer of peat. The sinking continued, but the redistribution of sediments could no longer keep pace. The area near the present juncture of Willow Creek and the Red Deer passed under water and became a bay, with its mudflats, tidal channels, and oyster banks. The major streams then returned to the region, depositing the deltaic silts, sands and coals now exposed near the top of the Red Deer River valley.

Deltaic sediments continued to be deposited until an uninterrupted sequence about 350 feet thick accumulated. These sediments, with their bands of black coal, white sandstone, and brown and ochre siltstone, are perhaps the most colourful strata exposed along any prairie river in western Canada. They are visible in the valley walls of the Red Deer from Willow Creek upstream beyond Drumheller for a total of nearly 30 miles. The coals have been of major importance in the establishment and growth of

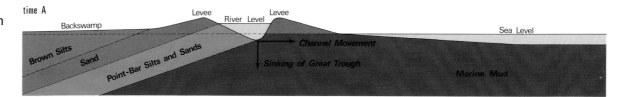

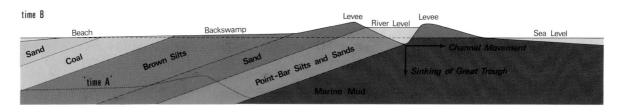

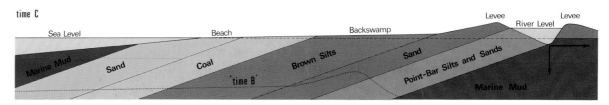

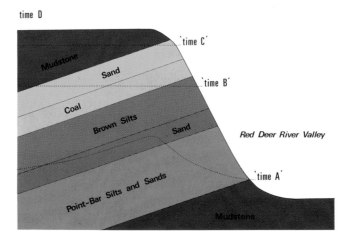

Pale river sands alternating with darker coal-swamp deposits, Horseshoe Canyon Formation, south bank of the Red Deer River, Alberta, opposite Willow Creek (S72-4024)

Variegated deltaic sediments of the lower Horseshoe Canyon Formation in the foreground, with the transition into coastal-plain sediments high in the bluffs on the opposite side of the Red Deer River valley north of Drumheller, Alberta (S72-2107)

Alternating stream sands, flood-plain silts and backswamp coals, lower Horseshoe Canyon Formation, Horsethief Canyon north of Drumheller, Alberta (S72-2091)

Drumheller, and the skeletons of over 50 dinosaurs have been quarried from the silts and sands. One of these, which was installed in the National Museum in Ottawa in 1913, was the first dinosaur skeleton to be mounted in Canada. A small but excellent museum operated by the Drumheller and District Museum Society receives as many as 3,000 visitors daily at the height of the tourist season to see the fossil remains of plants and animals that lived near Drumheller some 71 million years ago. Upon leaving the museum and passing through the fossil stumps in the parking lot, one can see the vivid hues of the river valley in the distance, which are enhanced by the rays of the setting sun and the clear blue prairie sky. As is so often the case, the present shape and beauty of the colourful strata mask the appearance of the very different world in which they were formed.

Wetland Forests
When the sediments surrounding Drumheller were being deposited, the region was about 150 miles east of the Rockies, and probably no more than 25 miles from the sea. It was situated on the southern edge of a large, approximately semicircular delta that projected more than 200 miles into the

Fossil stump probably belonging to a tree of the bald-cypress family, lower Horseshoe Canyon Formation near Drumheller, Alberta (S72-4113)

Detail of cross-section of stump (S72-4048)

interior sea. Streams laden with fine sediment flowed across the delta. As they slowly moved sideways toward lower areas in the delta, they left a characteristic pattern of sedimentary layers behind them. The cutting edge of the channels was steep where the bank was scoured by the force of the current. Sloping layers of sand and silt, or point-bar deposits, accumulated on the opposite, more gently inclined bank. As the stream continued to move in the direction of the cutting edge of the channel, nearly horizontal layers of silt and mud were deposited on top of the point-bar sands when water overflowed the banks. Finally a swamp developed, and, as the accumulation of plant remains began to exceed that of muds from the river, peat was formed, later to become coal.

The swamps often remained undisturbed for thousands of years, creating peat deposits that formed coal seams up to 13 feet thick. However, the land continued to sink, and streams swept across all parts of the delta many times, leaving behind layers of sand, silt, mud, and finally coal, as signatures of their passing. During all of this time the region was an enormous low-lying wetland of shallow lakes, swamps and marshes, traversed by streams that fanned out from the major river courses to the edges of the delta.

Today, broad-leaved trees usually dominate Canadian forests where soils are limey and moist but well-drained, and where forest fires seldom occur. Conversely, forests

The modern Mississippi Delta and associated bald-cypress and hard-wood forests. Note that the western coast of Louisiana has been rotated to the north.

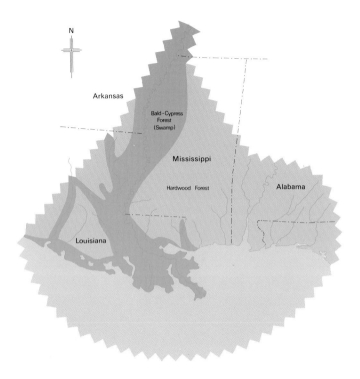

The western interior of Canada about 71 million years ago. The Mississippi Delta, as shown on the left, has been reversed, rotated and superimposed on southern Alberta to show the extent of the ancient delta.

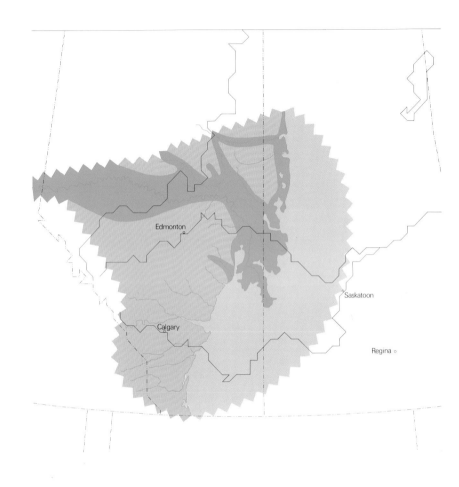

Swamp hardwoods, Ocala National Forest, Florida (S72-1891)

of conifers, or cone-bearing trees, grow where the soils are acidic and saturated with water because of high rainfall or poor drainage, or where forest fires occur frequently. The beech–maple woods of Ontario and the great douglas-fir–hemlock forests of British Columbia illustrate the differences in the forest cover of these two environments.

Broad-leaved trees would not have grown well in many regions of the ancient delta. The sands and silts were derived from acidic rocks in the interior of British Columbia. These were mixed with large quantities of extremely fine volcanic ash, also acidic, that were blown eastwards from volcanoes in the Rockies. Following volcanic eruptions in the west, ash falling in swamps, lakes and bays was often preserved in thin layers in the coals and mudstones. Large areas of the delta were covered by standing or slow-moving water, and although there was probably a cool, somewhat drier season, the air was always moist. The combination of a humid climate, acidic soils, and extensive areas of poorly drained land probably favoured the growth of conifers over most of the delta.

These wetlands were dominated by a special group of conifers that, more than any other, typified the lowland forests of the West during the last part of the age of reptiles. Indeed, the feather-like blue-green fronds of these plants would at that time have merited a central position on the flag of Canada just as the maple leaf does today. These trees are no longer spread over vast regions of the earth, and some are virtually extinct. They may be found growing naturally in certain areas of Tasmania, China, Japan, Mexico, and the United States. Of the surviving forms, two grow only 10 to 40 feet high, but the remaining seven attain heights in excess of 150 feet. One reaches the towering height of 368 feet, the tallest plant on earth. All of them are members of the bald-cypress family, or Taxodiaceae, and include the swamp cypresses, redwoods, dawn redwoods, giant sequoias, china firs, and a few other trees. Their wood resists the attacks of insects, fire, decay and disease, and the trees often survive to great ages. They prefer warm, wet, frost-free climates, and some thrive in swamps, where the roots of other trees would drown. In many ways they were worthy botanical counterparts of the dinosaurs.

In deltas, the extent to which a soil is drained is very important in determining the kinds of plants that will grow there. Accordingly, an increase in elevation of a few inches in these low wetlands may be accompanied by a greater change in forest vegetation than will an increase of a few hundred feet in mountainous regions. In the

ancient delta near Drumheller, the silts and sands deposited by flood waters along the rivers and in alluvial fans radiating from low areas of the river banks evidently produced moist but well-drained soils. The forests growing on them differed markedly from those of the surrounding swamps.

The fossil wood, fronds and cones found on these slightly more elevated areas indicate that the most abundant trees were redwoods, close relatives of the modern coast redwoods of California. Growing among them, but less abundant, were other evergreen conifers such as china firs, also belonging to the bald cypress family, and torreyas. In view of the size of their modern relatives and the favourable environmental conditions prevailing at that time, it would be surprising if these evergreens did not dominate the areas separating stream from swamp, as well as the better-drained regions throughout the delta. Today's massive coast redwoods grow close together, shutting out most of the sunlight. Their lowest branches are often more than 70 feet above the ground. The forest floor is blanketed with a carpet of mosses and luxuriantly growing ferns. Walking beneath a stand of these trees on the ancient delta, one would have experienced the

feeling of being in an enormous natural vault where the upper reaches of the cool, moist air were occasionally stabbed by shafts of sunlight. The soft mosses and delicate ferns would have muted footfalls on the gently undulating floor of the silent forest.

Between the redwood groves and the streams, on more recently deposited levee and overbank sediments, was a band of many different kinds of non-coniferous plants. Those lining the stream itself were possibly low, large-leaved gunneras and many varieties of sun-loving ferns. Behind them, on slightly higher ground, were cycad-like plants and katsura trees of progressively greater age. These trees, which are the largest broad-leaved trees in modern China, attaining heights of 120 feet, may well have been draped with vines of wild grape, moonseed and greenbriars. Seedlings and saplings of china firs and redwoods probably grew in the shade of the broad-leaved plants, indicating that the conifers would eventually replace them.

Relatively poorly drained ground on the opposite side of the redwood groves may have constituted another area where the conifers were not always able to dominate the forests. Here the soil was too wet to provide optimum growing conditions for redwoods, but too dry to permit the development of a cypress swamp. These regions were probably covered, at least periodically, by broad-leaved forests of ash, swamp hickory, and

Sunrise over bald-cypress swamp,
south channel from Lake Maurepas,
Louisiana (S73-639)

swamp oak. The trees were too
far away from the water courses
for their leaves to be blown into
streams, where they could have
been preserved from decay and
fossilized. Nevertheless, their
presence, and that of other plants
in the region, is indicated by fossil
pollen, which was more widely distributed by insects and the wind.
The broad-leaved, drier swamp forests, as well as nearby areas where
the evergreen canopy was broken
by the fall of a giant conifer, may
also have supported many varieties
of subtropical bushes and small
trees. Fossil pollen of the box,
myrtle, sweetleaf, protea, and
poison-ivy families has been recovered in abundance from the
deltaic sediments. Again, because
of an abundance of many kinds of
briars and vines, these broad-leaved
forests may have contained virtually impenetrable jungles of undergrowth.

Among the fossil stumps and
blocks of petrified wood found in
coal seams near Drumheller are
those of the bald cypress, a tree
that grows today in swamps and
deltas along the southern Atlantic
and Gulf coasts of the United
States. These trees, with their often
grotesquely buttressed bases, con-
torted trunks and spreading crowns,
must have grown in dense stands
in the regions of the ancient delta
that were covered by water for
most of the year. During the cool

Wax myrtle, Big Cypress Swamp, Florida (S72-1875)

Bald-cypress swamp southeast of Baton Rouge, Louisiana (S73-595)

*Bald-cypress swamp southeast of
Baton Rouge, Louisiana (S73-632)*

season the branchlets of the bald cypresses, and those of the smaller Chinese swamp cypresses growing with them, turned to a rusty orange colour and were shed. The many different varieties of epiphytes, or air plants, that flourished in the higher, more fully illuminated levels of the forest would then have been clearly visible. They were members of the mistletoe family, whose modern representatives grow in abundance in the tropics, but also form globular clumps of evergreen leaves on trees of the southeastern United States.

The forest canopy closed during the long, wet summers as the trees produced a new growth of dense, dark-green fronds. The waters below, stained to a deep tea-colour by dyes from cypress bark, were veiled by a thin, easily broken carpet of tiny floating ferns. The rotting logs of giant fallen cypresses were covered with larger ferns, or perhaps with giant-leaved gunnera plants where sunlight reached the surface of the swamp through a rent in the canopy. Over the course of many thousands of years, a thick, mucky layer of peat would accumulate beneath such a swamp. Ghostly lights, or foxfire, caused by burning methane exhaled from decomposing vegetation or smouldering peat, would frequently have illuminated the deep darkness of the humid summer nights. As the Great Dismal Swamp in Virginia appeared to a map-maker who explored it in 1670, most of the ancient delta would have looked to us like a "very large swamp or bogg ... a horrible desart ... [where] the foul Damps ascend without ceasing, corrupt the Air, and render it unfit for Respiration .... Never was Rum, that cordial of Life, found more necessary than in this Dirty Place."* In 1866, a visitor to the Atchafalaya Basin in Louisiana, a similar swamp, said that "the trees closing together at the top shut out the light, so that the weird and funereal aspect of the place is perfect, representing a forbidding appearance sufficient to appal a stranger."**

Denizens of Ancient Swamps

The sediments deposited in the deltaic wetlands do not contain the abundance of fish and small-animal remains found in the sediments of Dinosaur Provincial Park. Perhaps this is because the density of the forest canopy shut out the light necessary for the growth of vegetation in the understorey, thus depriving the smaller creatures of food and shelter. The swamps may also have been difficult for the smaller land animals to penetrate, and the large amounts of tannic acid draining into the swamp waters from tree barks would have been harmful to many varieties of aquatic organisms.

Animal life was probably not abundant in the outer regions of the swamps, near the edge of the sea. A few tyrannosaurs and some horned dinosaurs may have followed the drier levees deep into the swamplands, but most of the bones deposited there were washed downstream on the bottoms of rivers, together with an occasional partially disintegrated carcass. One dinosaur that probably did inhabit the outer, more open marshland forests was the peculiar large-horned dinosaur *Pachyrhinosaurus.* Instead of horns, this animal bore a huge cratered bony protuberance on its muzzle and a similar but smaller boss above each eye. Spines were evidently present along the rim of the neck shield. Scattered vertebrae and limb bones found in the vicinity of *Pachyrhinosaurus* skulls indicate that the reptile approached 20 feet in length and weighed as much as a large elephant. A blow from the massive head of an adult would probably have been ample to stun its tyrannosaurian contemporaries. Whether or not the animal herded, the circumstances of its preservation suggest that *Pachyrhinosaurus* lived apart from most other dinosaurs, on the outer reaches of the delta.

Although the backswamp areas away from the sea were frequented by several kinds of dinosaurs, by far the most abundant form was the duckbilled dinosaur *Edmontosaurus.*

* William Byrd, *The Westover manuscripts: containing the History of the dividing line betwixt Virginia and North Carolina....* (Peterburg, Va.: Ruffin, 1841), 143 pp. [As quoted in Dismal Swamp, *Contact,* vol. 8, no. 1 (Wayne, N.J.: Union Camp Corp., 1973), 24 pp.]

** M. L. Comeaux, *Atchafalaya Swamp life: settlement and folk occupations,* Geoscience and Man, vol. 2 (Louisiana State University, Baton Rouge: School of Geoscience, 1972), 111 pp.

Relatively well-drained deltaic
stream deposits grading upwards
into coastal-plain sediments,
Horseshoe Canyon Formation, Red
Deer River north of Drumheller,
Alberta (S72-4015)

These large animals, often more than 30 feet long, were primitive in appearance, lacking any special ornamentation on their horselike heads and having bodies less deep than those of some crested forms. The fossilized stomach contents of a closely related dinosaur suggest that *Edmontosaurus* almost certainly fed on the foliage of members of the bald-cypress family and on broad-leaved trees. The presence of these creatures in the swamplands probably produced a browse line about ten feet above the ground, or four to five feet above the high-water level. During times of low water, they must have ranged deeply into the swamps, cleaning out thickets of broad-leaved plants and stripping ferns and sapling trees. An impression left in the once soggy peat by a broad, three-toed foot, and subsequently filled with sand, indicates that the largest animals occasionally approached the outer edges of the delta.

It is easy to visualize an *Edmontosaurus* group walking and browsing in the misty, blue-green understorey of the swamp forest. Their size and the deliberation of their movements probably gave them a curiously cowlike majesty. What would they have done when the forest and swamp waters were blanketed with white volcanic ash? How would they have survived the violent storms that from time to time shattered the swamp forest over wide areas? Has there ever been a swampland at once quasi-familiar and yet so strange, fascinating and foreboding as this ancient delta, which vanished long before the memory of man began?

The duckbilled dinosaur Edmonto-saurus *in a bald-cypress swamp near Drumheller, Alberta*

A Coastal Plain

After a few hundred thousand years, the main areas of deltaic growth began to shift to the north. In the region of Drumheller the distributary channels no longer carried heavy loads of sediment, and the levees bordering the rivers became smaller. Their effect in disrupting drainage on the delta was correspondingly reduced. The peat-producing swamps were drained, and the bald-cypress forests that had dominated the area could no longer maintain themselves. As the influence of the delta lessened in the region of Drumheller, that of a long, narrower coastal plain extending northward along the mountains from Montana began to increase. This plain was fed by streams flowing from lime-rich rocks in the foothills of the mountains. Thus, the character of the soils changed from acidic and poorly drained to less acidic and better drained, providing conditions more favourable to the growth of broad-leaved trees.

The rivers that flowed across the region of Drumheller became smaller, and with the reduction in sediment supply the delta front began to retreat landwards. The former edge of the delta may have been replaced by an arc of offshore islands, and a shallow lagoon probably spread over the old marshlands near the sea. Brackish-water

Fern, liverworts and tree roots, Tunica Hills north of Weyanoche, Louisiana (S73-571)

bays extended as far inland as the region of the Red Deer valley north of Drumheller, where hard, lime-rich layers of sand and oyster shells form a band of ledges amid the softer, stream-deposited silts and clays. These broad environmental changes were accompanied by similar changes in the plant and animal communities living in the region.

A few fossil leaves from the Red Deer valley northwest of Drumheller, more from similar sediments of the ancient coastal plain to the south, and an abundance of pollen grains preserved in the mudstones and siltstones provide hints of the vegetation that covered the region at that time. The fossil pollens indicate that many different varieties of broad-leaved trees were present. However, these plants were in an early, rapidly evolving phase of their history, and had not yet dominated the lowland forests of warm-temperate and subtropical areas to the extent they do today. Conifers and several more-primitive kinds of trees and shrubs were also abundant. This mixture of ancient and more-modern trees, typical of the forests of that age, is nowhere duplicated today. Living forests that probably resemble them to some degree occur in southeastern China, and to a lesser extent in the southeastern United States and certain areas of central America. Nevertheless, the more-primitive plant groups that were once so abundant in Alberta are now scattered throughout the widely separated lands of the southern hemisphere. Let us try to imagine how these ancient forests might have looked.

An Ancient Forest of Broad-leaved Trees

The sun is bright on the sand bank near the edge of the stream and the air is hot and dry, for the dry season has begun. It is more pleasant in the deep shade of the dawn redwoods growing abundantly along the stream banks. Decaying branches lying on the moist, moss-covered ground are draped with tongue-shaped liverworts. Young trees and a few multicoloured mushrooms are sprouting from fallen, rotting trunks. In more-open areas within the groves are dense tangles of ferns, vine-laden shrubs, and woody lianas. Through the now rusty-coloured foliage and the straight, uptilted branches of the dawn redwoods, the green spires of isolated giant redwoods can be seen receding in the distance, tracing the course of the stream across the plain.

Lycopods and cortinarius mush-
room, near Limoges, Ontario
(S75-1390)

Pleurotus mushrooms on a decaying
elm trunk, near Limoges, Ontario
(S75-1391)

Katsura tree, Arboretum, Central Experimental Farm, Ottawa (S75-1389)

Ginkgo in fruit, Arboretum, Central Experimental Farm, Ottawa (S75-1388)

Away from the dawn-redwood groves along the stream, the forest abruptly becomes lower and more open. The light more easily penetrates the oval yellow leaves of the open-crowned katsuras and the yellow fan-shaped leaves of the ginkgoes. The carpet of ferns on the forest floor below is dotted with these yellow leaves. Interspersed among the other trees are breadfruit and protea, whose green, leathery leaves are subdivided into straps and remain on the trees throughout the year. The air carries the acrid odour of fallen ginkgo fruit, and the kaleidoscopic effect of shiny green and brilliant golden leaves linking the blue sky with the darker tree trunks and the forest soil is bewildering.

The ginkgo–katsura forest does not extend far from the stream, being gradually replaced by a denser forest containing numerous varieties of broad-leaved trees. Many of these are magnolias, some of which have shiny green leaves, which they will retain until after

Ginkgo and evergreen magnolia,
Baton Rouge, Louisiana (S73-556)

Protea leaves, Fairchild Garden,
Florida (S72-1872)

Magnolia in flower, Montreal
(S75-1387)

Mixed hardwood forest with tulip trees, evergreen magnolias, tupelos, red maples, oaks, elders, and poison-ivy and honeysuckle vines, near Saucier, Mississippi (S73-603)

A devil's-walking-stick in flower beside a pine tree, with a hardwood forest in the background, Hattiesburg, Mississippi (S73-585)

Mixed hardwood forest with evergreen and big-leaf magnolias, beeches, hop hornbeams, and honeysuckle and greenbrier vines, Hattiesburg, Mississippi (S73-633)

Oaks, hickories, osage orange trees, and climbing vines, Baton Rouge, Louisiana (S73-549)

Small big-leaf magnolia and red-bay trees within a beech–magnolia forest in the Ragland Hills southeast of Hattiesburg, Mississippi (S73-552)

Pines and big-leaf magnolias surrounded by a forest of evergreen magnolias, beeches, hickories, oaks and sycamores, with dogwoods, holly, anis trees, hop hornbeams and silver bells growing in the understorey, Ragland Hills southeast of Hattiesburg, Mississippi (S73-558)

new growth begins. Others have enormous silver-brown leaves, which are beginning to fall to the ground. These are often caught in the branches of young trees and in spider webs, giving the forest a peculiar layered appearance. The dark tupelo trees are now nearly bare, most of their scarlet foliage having fallen to the ground around them, although a few brilliantly coloured leaves are still attached to the branches. At infrequent intervals a few beech trees may be seen, their jagged-edged brown leaves adhering to branches that project horizontally from the smooth grey trunks, accentuating the stratified appearance of the forest. Rising high above the rest of the forest are the yellowing crowns of giant tulip trees. Woody lianas and vines of the honeysuckle and poison-ivy families disappear into the lower branches of the canopy, which also support dense clumps of epiphytes, or air plants. Closer to the ground are smaller, spiny-leaved holly trees, other broad-leaved evergreen shrubs, and immature trees. The forest floor is littered with yellow, red, and coarse brown leaves.

The hardwood forest covers much of the moist soil in the general vicinity of the stream courses. In wetter areas, bordered by tree ferns, the forest takes on a reddish

Immature pine–oak forest, Ocala National Forest, Florida (S72-1896)

Araucaria, Fairchild Garden, Florida (S72-1915)

hue from the turning fronds and leaves of dawn redwoods, tupelo and ash trees.

Beyond the hardwoods, to the west, the sky is smoky from distant ground fires. Here the soils are drier, and support mixed stands of needle-bearing pines, araucarias and podocarps. Present in abundance in the understorey are large cycad-like plants, their stocky trunks sometimes crowned with brightly coloured cones surrounded by deep-green palm-like fronds. Clumps of bushy quassia trees are also scattered through the region. Their long, sumac-like fronds have turned brown and are falling to the ground. The floor of the open forest is covered with a springy layer of bark fragments, spiny dead leaves, and dried cycad and quassia fronds. If it is ignited this year by lightening, the ensuing fire may spread into the edges of the hardwood forest. The ground fires do not seriously damage the open forest of ancient needle-bearing trees. It will kill hardwoods, however, restricting the hardwood forest to the moister regions of the coastal plain.

Hardwoods and Dinosaurs
The ancient coastal plain was more heavily forested, was closer to the sea, and probably lacked the varied wetland environments that had existed among the meandering streams of Dinosaur Provincial Park. Nearly 90 dinosaur specimens have been collected from sediments that were deposited on the

Podocarpus, Baton Rouge,
Louisiana (S73-573)

The cycads Encephalartos lehmanni
and Cycas circinalis, *Fairchild*
Garden, Florida (S72-1908)

The cycad Cycas media, *Fairchild Garden, Florida (S72-1861)*

surface of the coastal plain. They represent all of the major kinds of dinosaurs found in Dinosaur Provincial Park. Some, such as the ostrich and duckbilled dinosaurs, were apparently much more abundant on the forested plain, while others, including the tyrannosaurs and the armoured and horned dinosaurs, were less so.

However, 5 million years had elapsed since the dinosaurs of the Park had lived, and their descendants of the forested plain were no longer quite the same. Only those reptiles surviving to maturity, and therefore more perfectly suited to their environments, had sired the hatchlings of new generations. The environments were in turn subject to the dynamic relationships linking a slowly changing landscape with the many kinds of competing plants and animals living on it, and could not remain unaltered. Over long periods of time these slow processes of change and adjustment produced changes in the habits and appearance of the races of dinosaurs.

Thus, the skeletal remains of a helmeted duckbilled dinosaur, descended from *Corythosaurus,* are found buried in the fossil channels and point-bars of streams that crossed the coastal plain. Its young are also preserved in the same river-bank deposits. *Hypacrosaurus,* as it has been named, possesses

The cycad Encephalartos ferox,
Fairchild Garden, Florida
(S72-1859)

in exaggerated form some of the peculiarities of its ancestor. Most strikingly, the backbone arches slightly upwards in front of the hips and then curves downwards to the base of the neck, which is held at knee level. The spines of the backbone are extremely long, giving the animal the appearance of a gigantic razor-backed turkey with a long, heavy tail. The thigh and forearm are also somewhat longer than in the ancestral form, and the narial passageways within the crest on its head are more completely encased in bone.

Hypacrosaurus evidently lived in the broad-leaved forests near the streams. Like its contemporary, *Edmontosaurus,* it consumed woody shrubs and ferns, cleaning out the undergrowth and probably producing a browse line some seven or eight feet above the ground. It avoided the cypress swamps, for the ranges of these two dinosaurs were mutually exclusive. The skeleton of *Hypacrosaurus* gives the impression that the animal must have been an excellent walker. Perhaps it emerged from the forest at dawn to bask along the stream banks. There the sun-warmed blood circulating through the fleshy web between the long spines on its back would reheat the body. Returning to the cooler forest, it may have traversed large areas in the course of a day, regulating its body temperature by its activity and control of the blood flow through its narrow

The duckbilled dinosaur Hypacrosaurus *in a broad-leaved forest near*
Trochu, Alberta

back. The trumpeting of neighbours, its own swift pace, and its ability to cope with more extreme temperatures served to protect *Hypacrosaurus* from the attacks of tyrannosaurs.

Ostrich dinosaurs abounded in the open forests of the coastal plain. Their footprints have been recovered from sands bordering the brackish-water bayous, and their delicate bones occur in sediments deposited along streams that once flowed through the broad-leaved woods. They were doubtless at home in the drier evergreen forests as well, and their skeletons have also been collected from the stream courses of the cypress swamps. The ostrich dinosaurs were all excellent runners. It would, indeed, be more correct to think of ostriches as imitators of these long-extinct reptiles. In some respects the modern large ground birds may not have equalled them in the perfection of their adaptation to a running mode of locomotion.

Dromiceiomimus, the most common ostrich dinosaur in the broad-leaved forests of the ancient coastal plain, was about as large as a medium-sized ostrich. With its birdlike bill it captured small animals uncovered by raking the ground litter with the elongated claws on its three-fingered hands.

Its brain was as large as that of an ostrich, but its eyes were much larger than the ostrich's, surpassing those of any living land animal. An extremely powerful set of muscles suspended from the base of the tail like the rigging on the mast of a sailing vessel provided the main force for pulling the hind limbs backwards. The strength and arrangement of the muscles in the hips of *Dromiceiomimus* and the length of the legs suggest that the animal could run faster than the ostrich, which has been clocked at 50 miles an hour. The thigh could not turn in and out as freely at the hip joint as can that of an ostrich, and an ostrich dinosaur could not have dodged nearly as readily. However, the combination of extremely keen eyesight, relatively high level of intelligence, and extraordinary running ability must have made *Dromiceiomimus* a very difficult animal to capture. Interestingly, the pelvic canal is very broad, suggesting that the young may have been born alive. Some parental care is indicated by the association of an adult *Dromiceiomimus* with two juvenile specimens, buried together in a layer of silty sand.

Other ostrich dinosaurs may not have been so fleet of foot as *Dromiceiomimus*. *Struthiomimus* was a heavier animal, and its forelimbs were much stronger. Its remains are more frequently found in the river deposits of Dinosaur Provincial Park than in those of the later coastal plain, and the animal

may have preferred more bushy surroundings. Perhaps it ripped decaying logs apart with its powerful foreclaws to search for wood-boring insects, or excavated buried nests of turtle or crocodile eggs, as these reptiles were abundant in the Park. Only three specimens of *Ornithomimus* have been collected in western Canada, one from the sediments of the Park, and two others from those of the cypress delta. It was a lightly built animal with slender hands and arms, and with legs that were not quite as strong as those of *Dromiceiomimus*. Perhaps it depended more on coloration and retiring habits for protection. All together, the combination of the forearms of an anteater, the head and legs of a flightless ground-bird, and the body and tail of a reptile must have made the ostrich dinosaurs one of the most interesting and peculiar groups of ancient reptiles.

Anchiceratops had replaced *Chasmosaurus* as the commonest horned dinosaur in the stream-bank environments of the coastal plain. It also inhabited the edges of the bayous, or brackish-water bays, and followed the levees into the cypress delta. It too was rhino size, and resembled *Chasmosaurus* in most respects, although its body

The ostrich dinosaur
Dromiceiomimus *in a redwood*
grove near Trochu, Alberta

was somewhat longer and the tail relatively short. The head of *Anchiceratops* differed in that the horns over each eye were long and slender, and tongue-shaped bony projections were present on the back of the neck shield. Deep within the skull, imbedded in the bone on each side of the brain, was a cluster of three tiny semicircular canals. It is from these organs that all land-dwelling backboned animals, including man, derive their sense of balance. Two of the canals are vertical in position, and the third is always horizontal. By noting the position of the horizontal canal in *Anchiceratops*, it is apparent that the animal normally held its head at an angle to the ground, looking ahead between the tips of its brow and nose horns. It is difficult to reconstruct the feeding habits of the animal. Perhaps it turned its head sideways to seize small clumps of plants, such as ferns, by the stems, and then righted its head, simultaneously pulling upwards and snapping off the crowns or uprooting the entire plant. In a similar way it could have cropped off the crowns of tree ferns, after toppling them with its body. The softer fronds would then be chopped up and swallowed, and the more woody tissues ejected from the mouth. Perhaps *Anchiceratops* also plucked the large, brilliantly coloured cones of cycads from among the poisonous fronds, for the seeds are important in the diet of monkeys living where cycads grow today.

The fleshy outer coat of the seeds would be digested, and the stony kernels would pass undamaged through the digestive tract of the reptile.

The duckbilled dinosaur *Saurolophus* frequented the shores of the bayous that notched the margin of the coastal plain. Its body resembled that of *Edmontosaurus*, but the head possessed a broader, more spatulate beak. The profile of the muzzle rose in a nearly straight line above the eyes, and then curved upwards into a long spine. *Saurolophus* had descended from a relatively rare dinosaur from the more ancient river courses of Dinosaur Provincial Park, *Prosaurolophus*, which bore an incipiently developed spine in front of its eyes. A skeleton of *Saurolophus* excavated by the American Museum of Natural History in 1911 was the first essentially complete dinosaur skeleton to be collected in Canada. Its discovery greatly stimulated the search for dinosaurs in the western provinces. The animal had died and come to rest with its head lying in a pool of water. Wavelets had gently washed the bones of the neck and forefeet from the decaying flesh, slightly scattering them, and surrounded the skull with a halo of ripple marks. Curiously, another *Saurolophus* skeleton, discovered in 1948 by Russian collectors working in Mongolia, helped to kindle a renewed interest in the dinosaurs of central Asia. The Mongolian species was the larger of the two, growing to lengths of over 40 feet and possessing a longer cranial spine.

Many other dinosaurs inhabited the coastal plain. The tyrannosaur *Albertosaurus* had longer legs than its ancestor in the Park, and the already tiny forelimbs had become even smaller. Improvements in the fleetness and armour of their contemporaries reflect the deadly effectiveness of these large predators. The legs of half-grown albertosaurs were relatively longer than in the adults, an adaptation that may have enabled them to capture smaller, more fleet animals, perhaps even ostrich dinosaurs. As the carnivores matured, they grew more powerful and altered their habits to prey on the larger herbivores. The short-faced horned dinosaur *Arrhinoceratops* and several varieties of armoured dinosaurs were also present, but uncommon. The remains of smaller animals, such as the boneheaded pachycephalosaurs, dromaeosaurs and stenonychosaurs, are rarely found. One seven-foot skeleton of a small, running herbivore, *Parksosaurus*, has been collected. This animal may have dwelt among bushier growth in the drier evergreen forests.

The evidence preserved in the valley of the Red Deer River near Drumheller provides a fascinating glimpse of a small part of the earth's surface as it was 71 million years ago. The animals and plantscapes of that time would have

The duckbilled dinosaur
Saurolophus, *with a plesiosaur in*
the background, along a brackish-
water bayou near Trochu, Alberta

appeared at once almost familiar
and very strange to us. Yet the web
of interrelationships between
plants, animals and the land was
like that which controls the distribution of plants and animals today.
Duckbilled dinosaurs grazing on
the stream banks and in the forests
kept them relatively free of undergrowth. Ostrich dinosaurs could
then live there, for their vision and
speed would not be impaired by a
dense ground cover. Tyrannosaurs
fed on the duckbills, keeping their
numbers in check so that they
would not destroy the forest
through overgrazing. The kind of
trees that could grow in an area
was determined by the composition
of its soil, the drainage, and the
presence or absence of bush fires.
The shade from the forest canopy
and the feeding habits of large
herbivorous dinosaurs produced a
more uniform ground environment,
thus reducing the variety of smaller
animals that could inhabit an area.
However, physical events such as
unusually severe storms, floods, or
rapidly eroding river systems
weakened the forest's grip on the
land, and provided niches for a host
of smaller ground-dwelling creatures. This intricate system of
checks and balances has long been
one of the greatest marvels of the
world, which we, for the passing
moment of a lifetime, are fortunate
to explore.

V The Last Dinosaurs

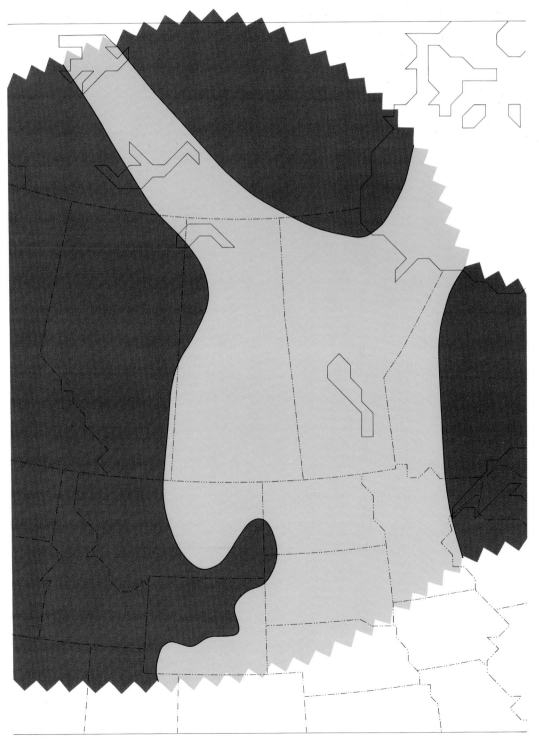

The western interior of North America about 70 million years ago

A Trough That Ceased to Sink

The channels of the northern delta, fanning out into the sea to the southeast, returned to the Drumheller region about 70 million years ago, and brought the bald-cypress swamps with them. Coastal-plain environments lingered briefly to the south, in the vicinity of Lethbridge. However, the western margin of the great trough gradually ceased to sink. Sediments from the northern river system quickly filled the basin of the shallow sea in eastern Alberta and western Saskatchewan. The coastline now followed the delta front from north-central Saskatchewan southwest to the Alberta–Saskatchewan border. Another large delta rapidly expanded northeastwards from Wyoming, reaching the Saskatchewan border south of Regina. A shallow arm of the sea, over 200 miles wide, lingered between the two deltas in central Montana and southwestern Saskatchewan for another million years.

Concurrently the climate was becoming warmer and more subtropical. This was reflected in a northward migration of shellfish and marine micro-organisms from the southern part of the seaway, near the Gulf of Mexico. A few specimens of the gigantic horned dinosaur *Triceratops* have been collected in sediments deposited in South Dakota as the delta spread

northeastwards from Wyoming. The western margin of the great trough rose slightly, and the arm of the sea between the two great deltas was drained. Under the influence of the warmer, moist climates, volcanic rocks in western Montana were deeply weathered to produce white clays. These clays were carried by streams to the north and east. Mixed with sands, silts and volcanic ash, they were spread into a broad, thin blanket of white sediments that extends from northern Montana to the Swan Hills of Alberta northwest of Edmonton, and east to the Missouri Coteau south of Regina. Leaves preserved in these sediments indicate that the region was covered by a forest of broad-leaved trees. Most of these — including the laurels, magnolias, tulip trees, dogwoods, and persimmons — bore leaves with smooth margins, indicating the existence of a warm, humid climate. The lakes were covered with water lilies and lotus.

The geography of the Prairie Provinces then changed in a remarkable way. The sediment carried eastwards by streams from the Rockies dwindled to insignificant amounts. Perhaps the major streams were diverted to other areas far to the north or south, or to the Pacific Ocean. The western shoreline of the interior sea had withdrawn to the vicinity of the Saskatchewan–Manitoba border, although the similarity between

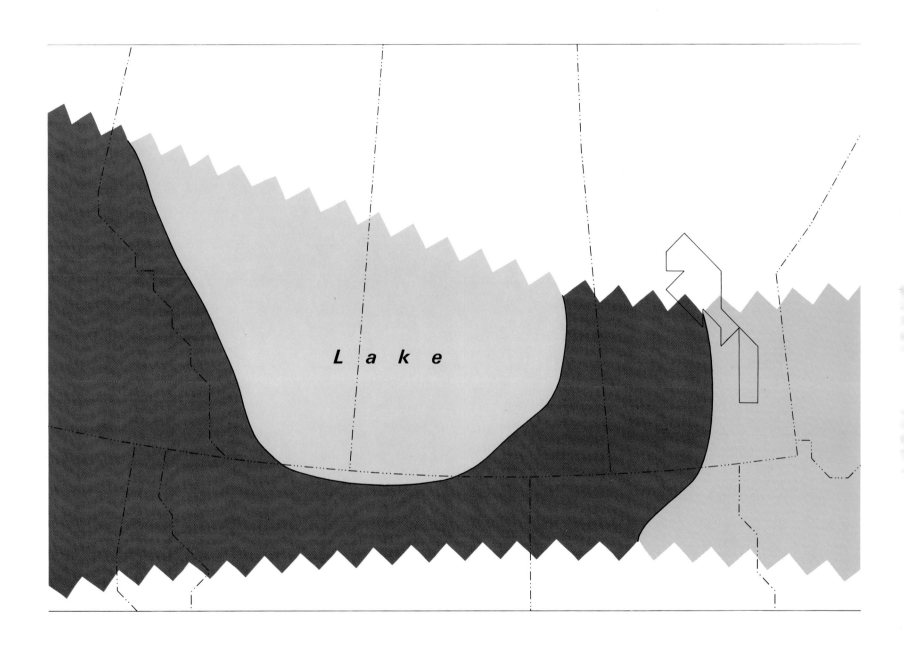

The western interior of Canada
about 66 million years ago

L a k e

Whitemud Formation lying between the highest wetland deltaic sediments of the Horseshoe Canyon Formation below and the dark lake-clays of the Battle Formation above, in Horseshoe Canyon near Drumheller, Alberta (S72-2094)

A detail of the olive-brown Frenchman Formation, whose sands mask the grey clays of the Battle Formation lying between it and the Whitemud Formation below. The lowermost coal can be seen to the left, on top of the olive-brown sands. On Ravenscrag Butte, Saskatchewan (S72-4121)

shellfishes living in the interior sea and those inhabiting marine waters near Greenland at that time indicates that the seaway still divided North America. A slight uplift along the eastern edge of the broad coastal plain was evidently accompanied by slight but very widespread sinking to the west. As a result of these movements, a vast freshwater lake was formed in Alberta and western Saskatchewan. A layer of dark mud was deposited on the blanket of white sediments beneath the lake. The dark mudstones are now known to extend for over 500 miles from just north of the Forty-ninth Parallel to the Peace River, and east to the Missouri Coteau. Ash blown from western volcanoes repeatedly fell into the lake, and one unusually thick layer was determined to be 66 million years old. Thus, 66 million years ago much of the western prairie was covered by a lake that rivalled Hudson Bay in size.

Four million years elapsed, and during this time little sediment accumulated in the western regions of the great trough in Canada. Vertical movements within the Rockies then re-elevated the mountain chain, although not to its present height. A subsidiary chain of smaller mountains appeared, extending from western Montana across Wyoming to the southeast. In Canada a simultaneous arching of the floor of the great trough

The youngest dinosaur-producing strata of the Scollard Member, also containing Triceratops, occur between the Whitemud and Battle formations below and the crest of the valley walls. The sediments in the centre foreground have been landslid toward the river. Near Scollard on the Red Deer River, Alberta (S72-4028)

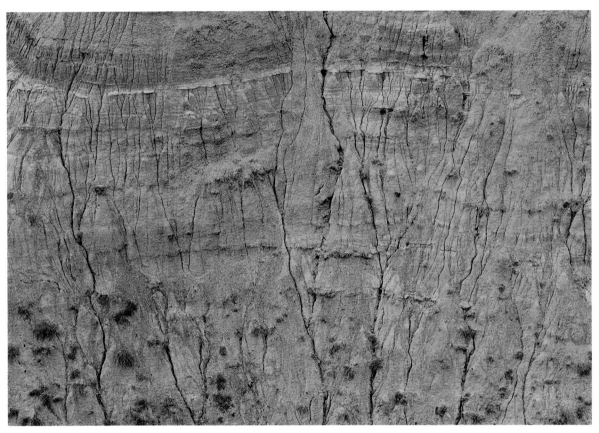

Floodplain sediments of the Scollard Member, near Scollard on the Red Deer River, Alberta (S72-3987)

paralleled the newly-formed ranges in Wyoming. The entire basin of the great lake was elevated, as were adjacent regions in eastern Montana. The lake was replaced by a series of low hills, which extended from the area around Drumheller and Red Deer, Alberta, southeast across the Cypress Hills and Wood Mountain regions of Saskatchewan into eastern Montana.

During the final one or two million years of the dinosaurs' existence, a great sheet of sediment spread from the mountains of southwestern Montana and Wyoming to the north and east. Much of this sediment was deposited in a slowly sinking trough in southern Montana. However, the quantity of silt and sand carried by the streams was so great that valleys over 100 feet deep in central Montana were quickly filled, as were the low hills in eastern Montana and in central Alberta near Drumheller. The hills of southern Saskatchewan stood out above the flood of sediment for a longer time. Although broad valleys more than 200 feet deep were filled, the summits of some hills remained above the surrounding floodplain until after the dinosaurs had vanished.

The western interior of Canada
about 65 million years ago

About 65 million years ago, then, a broad, low floodplain extended east from the foothills of the Rockies for 600 miles across southern Alberta and Saskatchewan and adjacent Montana. In the size and shape of its land surface, it somewhat resembled the Amazon River basin in western Brazil. However, the mountains to the west were nearer and not so high, and the region was probably drained by several river systems. To the east lay the interior sea, which had now shrunk to no more than 500 miles in width.

The surface of the floodplain was broader and more uneven than that of the older lowlands that had formerly separated the mountains from the sea. Local uplifts had produced low, but drier and better-drained, hills in several areas of the floodplain. Conversely, small and relatively short-lived lakes dotted regions where the moist plain tended to sink more rapidly than sediments could accumulate on the surface. Meandering across the broad, gently undulating floodplain, large rivers added further variety to the landscape. Their waters were heavily laden with sediment, which they repeatedly spread far beyond their banks during times of high water. Over most of the floodplain the rate of sedimentation was too high and the drainage too rapid to permit the development of peat bogs.

Bald cypress on the edge of a seasonally drained lake-bed, Lake Chicot, Louisiana (S73-634)

Wing-leaf soapberry, Everglades
National Park, Florida (S72-1881)

Slash pines, saw palmettos and
ferns, Big Pine Key, Florida
(S72-1877)

Life on a Subtropical Floodplain

Several kinds of subtropical plants
were present along the river
courses and lake shores that had
been absent or less abundant in
the older swamp and coastal-plain
forests near Drumheller. Among
these were fan palms, figs, and
small trees of the soapberry family.
Screw pines, with their long strap-
like leaves and stilted aerial roots,
and pond apples, with their con-
torted trunks, were also conspicu-
ous in the wet environments. All of
these plants suggest the existence
of warmer, more subtropical climates than had prevailed several
million years earlier over the same
region. Between the rivers, the
floodplains were covered with
swamps dominated by bald cypress,
tupelo, elm, and ash. Smaller areas
that escaped seasonal floods
probably supported forests of tulip
trees, magnolias and laurels. Here
the understorey was filled with
sassafras, soapberry and ginseng
trees. All of these forests supported lianas and vines, and the
branches of the trees were laden
with air plants, some of which
must have produced a profusion
of brilliant flowers.

Pollen from the plants on the
gently sloping hillsides was blown
into wetlands near the rivers. There
it was preserved, although the low

Immature bald-cypress forest with tupelos, palmettos and various epiphytes, Big Cypress Swamp, Florida (S72-1873)

Screw pines, Fairchild Garden, Florida (S72-1856)

The fig Ficus racemosa, Fairchild Garden, Florida (S72-1865)

Tupelo swamp near Opelousas,
Louisiana (S73-614)

Tupelo seedlings growing in a litter
of tupelo, bald-cypress and wild-
grape leaves, near Opelousas,
Louisiana (S73-636)

Open hardwood forest, Baton Rouge,
Louisiana (S73-563)

*Second-growth oaks and palmettos,
Ocala National Forest, Florida
(S72-1892)*

hills themselves were subsequently buried, or eroded away. This fossil pollen indicates the existence of an association of plants not duplicated anywhere on earth today, but perhaps most similar to the native forests of New Zealand. Among them were cone-bearing trees resembling giant club mosses, such as the rimus *(Dacrydium)* and araucaria. The fleshy-needled podocarps and related phylloclads, in which needles were replaced by green fan-like branches, were also represented. Tanoaks, primitive walnuts, and cycads, all reminiscent of warm-temperate floras of Asia, were present, as was the small-leaved southern beech *(Nothofagus)*, which like the araucaria survives only in Australasia and southern South America. Occurring with these exotic trees were larches and firs. In areas that were repeatedly burnt, pines and plants with protected underground stems, including some of the palmettos and cycads, were probably more abundant.

The muddy waters of the rivers were inhabited by aquatic animals, although far fewer varieties of bony fishes were present than there are today in streams of similar size. The most common aquatic animals were elongated swimming salamanders. Voracious three-foot-long bowfins were also abundant. Their large heads and heavy bodies contrasted with the elongate shapes of gars, although both forms preyed upon crayfish, smaller fishes, and other water-dwelling creatures. An occasional sturgeon or paddlefish hovered near the bottom in less turbulent parts of the rivers. Fragile bones buried in the ancient sands indicate that water birds resembling loons, sandpipers and flamingoes also followed the river courses to the sea.

The transition from the murky stream environments to those of the mature, open forest was very abrupt. Second-growth trees rapidly attained a large size on point-bars left behind by the rivers. On the opposite banks, large sections of the mature forest collapsed into the rivers with each season of high water. The animals that normally abounded in tangled, bushy vegetation along the stream banks, such as turtles, frogs and smaller dinosaurs, could not easily find a suitable environment. They were not abundant, and their remains are infrequently preserved. However, some small lizards and primitive squirrel-like mammals flourished in the trees, consuming insects, seeds and fruits. Indeed, a single tooth, slightly more than one-sixteenth of an inch long, collected in Montana, may have been derived from the lower jaw of a very primitive monkey.

The wetland forests between the rivers probably did not provide a hospitable environment for large animals. The structure of the mature forest must have been such that the branches of the broadleaved trees met some 50 to 100 feet above the ground to form a continuous canopy. The crowns of the taller bald cypresses and dawn redwoods overshadowed the surrounding trees from heights of at least 150 feet. Smaller plants on the forest floor were immersed in shade during the warm growing season, and submerged in water during the wetter months. The amount of ground vegetation available for consumption may not have been great, and probably varied throughout the year. In this respect, large areas of central Montana were similar to the outer regions of the delta that had existed 6 million years earlier near Drumheller. This portion of the delta had been populated by flat-headed duckbilled dinosaurs and large ram-nosed horned dinosaurs. A generally similar association of dinosaurs occurred in central Montana.

The most common dinosaur in the region was the great horned dinosaur *Triceratops,* but even it may not have been very abundant. Skulls and fragments of skeletons were scattered over the forest floor by scavengers and flood waters. Some of the bones were buried in sediments left behind by the floods, but most were partially or completely disintegrated by the elements before they could be fossilized. If, toward the end of the dry season, one could have explored the forest floor, then bathed in the bright, warm light of the early spring sun, it would have seemed somewhat deserted. Lizards scurried about on the tree trunks, and one might have been startled by the mock charge of a crayfish, its claws raised offensively, after inadvertently disturbing it in its shallow, leaf-choked puddle. In the course of perhaps an hour's walk, a greenish-white loglike object might be seen, partly buried in the wet soil. On closer inspection it would prove to be the 4-foot-long thighbone of a *Triceratops*. Less frequently, an enormous 7-foot skull might be found, its brow horns and neck frill fixing it upside-down in the ground. The teeth and the parrot-like bone at the end of the beak would have long since been lost to the elements, and the skull shrouded with mosses and liverworts. The reptiles that left these bones behind would be more difficult to find, although tracks, broken vegetation, and great fibrous droppings would be fairly frequently encountered. However, the noise of splintering wood and deep breathing as well as the great bulk of the animal would render its proximity obvious. They were bulkier than the largest elephants, although not quite so tall. Adults exceeded 25 feet in length and

9½ feet in height at the hips, and weighed more than 9 tons. Like other horned dinosaurs, they were no doubt protected by their head armour and an exceedingly bellicose disposition.

Perhaps because of the reduced extent of the broad-leaved hardwood forests that had flourished earlier on well-drained coastal plains, no duckbilled dinosaurs of the helmeted and spike-headed varieties have been collected from sediments deposited at this time on the floodplains of the Prairie Provinces or the adjacent states. Flat-headed duckbilled dinosaurs were present, although in fewer numbers than *Triceratops*. These animals have been named *Anatosaurus*. They possessed broader, more spatulate bills than did the flat-headed duckbilled dinosaurs of the older delta, and adults did not become quite as large. Mature animals were about 30 feet long and weighed about 3½ tons. Their remains are more closely associated with river sandstones than are those of *Triceratops*, and the skeletons that have been collected are more completely preserved. In two specimens the sediments contain skin impressions that nearly surround the skeletons. It is from these remarkable fossils that we know that *Anatosaurus* had webbed forefeet and a fleshy fringe along the midline of the back. The animals probably followed the river courses, stripping such young trees of the

wetland forest as they could find near the stream banks.

With *Triceratops* and *Anatosaurus* lived the largest terrestrial flesh-eating creature known to man, the celebrated *Tyrannosaurus*. Is there a child in North America who has not been filled with dreadful wonder at this long-extinct 40-foot monster, which weighed nearly 8 tons? How many parents have rescued a young son or daughter from its 4-foot jaws and 5½-inch-long teeth at the climax of a nightmare? *Tyrannosaurus* was named in 1905, and at present is known from only one partial skeleton, which lacks all of the limb bones but one, and from fewer than a dozen more-fragmentary skeletons. Most of the latter were collected in Montana, about 100 miles south of the international boundary. Only a few isolated bones have thus far been collected in Canada. Another smaller and more primitive species of *Tyrannosaurus* lived in central Asia at about the same time.

Like its Asian relative and North American predecessors, *Tyrannosaurus* may have preferred to hunt near the river courses. Most of the skeletal remains have been found in the sands that filled old valleys as the sheet of floodplain deposits spread northeastwards from southern Montana. Except for its size, the reptile did not differ greatly from more ancient tyrannosaurs.

Like them, it was a bipedal carnivorous automaton with tiny two-fingered forelimbs and a very small brain. However, *Tyrannosaurus* was a much heavier animal, and its hind limbs were more powerfully constructed. Certainly its strength was needed to bring down one of the large contemporary horned dinosaurs. Perhaps, like the modern Komodo lizard, its mouth was septic, so that its bite weakened or ultimately killed prey animals through infection or blood poisoning. They could then be easily overcome, or devoured as carrion at some later time. More likely, however, *Tyrannosaurus* killed its prey outright, after first disabling the horned dinosaur by tearing away pieces of the body of the living animal.

Isolated skulls of a most peculiar group of dinosaurs, the pachycephalosaurs, have also been discovered in the floodplain deposits extending south of the Forty-ninth Parallel. An incomplete skeleton of a smaller, more ancient pachycephalosaur from Dinosaur Provincial Park reveals that the bodies of these reptiles were broad and bore a long, slender tail like those of many other small bipedal dinosaurs. The front legs, however, were quite short, and the back was unusually strong. The body of the later form, *Pachycephalosaurus*,

The dome-headed dinosaur
Pachycephalosaurus *among giant*
gunnera leaves, with a large
podocarp, tree fern and screw pines
in the background. Near Wood
Mountain, Saskatchewan.

was probably similar, and the animal may have stood about as high as man.

The superficially human appearance did not end with its body. Above and behind the large eyes, the skull in some specimens rose to a rounded dome strikingly like that characteristic of a human skull. Wart-like bony projections covered the small nose and formed a fringe around the back of the head. In other specimens of *Pachycephalosaurus* the cranial dome was much lower. However, the brain was of normal dinosaurian proportions, and was protected by nine inches of very solid bone. It is assumed that male animals possessed the thicker domes, a postulate that will surely find some support among readers of the gentle sex, and that they butted their heads together as rams do during the rutting season. At other times they probably sought refuge in the forest in areas of windfalls and thick undergrowth, where they could escape from the larger carnivores. The size and shape of their teeth indicate that they browsed on soft vegetation, and the rarity of their remains suggests that the animals may not have been very numerous.

Thescelosaurus, another small herbivorous dinosaur, frequented stream-bank environments. They were short-limbed, had rather plump, rotund bodies, and grew to lengths of about 11 feet. Their heads were small, and the animals must have appeared at once curiously lizard- and bird-like as they gathered in brushy areas along streams

to feed on the foliage. Perhaps they darted into thickets or slipped into the water at the approach of a predator. A single skull of a small species of the tyrannosaur *Albertosaurus* has been collected, indicating that carnivorous reptiles of comparable size were also present.

Few other dinosaurs inhabited the floodplain forests. Only rarely have isolated bones of ostrich dinosaurs or eagle-clawed dromaeosaurs been found. One incompletely preserved skeleton of the giant armoured dinosaur *Ankylosaurus* was discovered in Montana. It is nearly half again as large as its precursor, *Euoplocephalus,* whose remains occur in older sediments along the Red Deer River. Like the latter, *Ankylosaurus* possessed a tail club, but it was a more massive animal and bore larger horn-like projections on the back of its skull. All together, skeletons of about 60 dinosaurs have been excavated in Montana and the Dakotas. Most of these belong to *Triceratops,* and hundreds of other bones of this giant horned dinosaur were bypassed because they were very poorly preserved. As is true of most of its dinosaurian associates, *Triceratops* was larger than the related forms that had formerly inhabited the lowlands west of the interior sea. The size of these later dinosaurs probably reflects the

generally warmer climates prevailing over the entire region at this time.

Sediments that long ago were spread to the northeast across the ancient floodplain have been re-exposed by the Frenchman River and the streams flowing southwards from Wood Mountain in southwestern Saskatchewan. Here the sediments filled ancient valleys and gradually encroached upon low hills standing above the general level of the floodplain. These hills were probably covered by the open forest of peculiar cone-bearing trees that apparently dominated the slightly more elevated areas at that time. Only about 17 dinosaur specimens have so far been collected from the floodplain deposits of this region. Most of these are isolated skulls of *Triceratops.* However, in the civic museum of Eastend, Saskatchewan, is the flat, rectangular neck shield of another giant horned dinosaur, *Torosaurus.* There are only three other skulls of this animal known from North America, and its skeletal remains have never been recognized. The anatomy of the neck shield suggests that *Torosaurus* was descended from the smaller *Chasmosaurus,* several skeletons of which have been collected in Dinosaur Provincial Park. The brow horns of *Torosaurus* are very long. Two specimens of the flat-headed duckbill *Anatosaurus* were discovered near Wood Mountain, as well as scattered *Thescelosaurus* bones. The association of dinosaurs that inhabited the floodplain surrounding the ancient hills of southwestern Saskatchewan was probably similar to the one that lived farther south, in Montana, at this time. Of the animals that lived on the hills, nothing is known.

Three hundred miles to the northwest, and 40 miles north of Drumheller, Alberta, sediments of the ancient floodplain may again be seen, high in the valley walls of the Red Deer River. These were the last sediments to be deposited in Alberta during the dinosaurian era. They were spread over a series of older sediments, now exposed along the Red Deer as it flows south. The latest of these were the dark clays of the ancient lake, preceded by the underlying thin white sandstone, the silts, coals and sands of delta–coastal-plain environments, the marine muds of a shallow sea, and finally the sands of the braided streams of Dinosaur Provincial Park. All together this series of sediments represents a span of 12 million years. It has yielded a greater variety of dinosaurian associations and a greater number of dinosaur skeletons than any other comparable series of sediments on earth.

The clays of the ancient lake in this region were usually not heavily eroded before they were again covered by silts and sands of the floodplain, and such hills as did exist were very low and quickly buried. The fossil pollen and leaves present indicate that the forests

here were similar to those in Montana, but the association of dinosaurs was not quite the same. Of the approximately 16 specimens discovered, only about one-third were of *Triceratops*. A single skeleton of *Thescelosaurus* has been collected, but no remains of duckbilled dinosaurs. Conversely, two specimens of the large armoured dinosaur *Ankylosaurus* are known, as well as six specimens of the small protoceratopsid *Leptoceratops,* which was about as large as a pig. In many respects *Leptoceratops* resembled the horned dinosaurs, but it lacked the horns and neck shield typically present in the larger reptiles.

In North America the skeletal remains of protoceratopsids usually occur in sediments deposited not far from mountainous regions, and in central Asia the eggs and skeletons of *Protoceratops* are known in abundance from ancient inland deposits. Armoured dinosaurs smaller than, but similar to, *Ankylosaurus* have been collected from windblown sands containing the nests of *Protoceratops*. The apparent abundance of protoceratopsids and ankylosaurs, the relatively fewer specimens of *Triceratops,* and the absence of *Anatosaurus* suggest that in the region of the Red Deer the floodplain was close to another major environment.

This is further supported by the presence of tiny fur-bearing mammals, for the seed-eating squirrel-like forms were much less common, and insectivores and the pouched opossum-like forms much more common, than in central Montana. These differences may have been a consequence of uplifts that occurred in the western mountains, probably near their present position about 100 miles to the west.

A Doomed Panorama

Fragmentary remains of duckbilled dinosaurs have been discovered 1,200 miles to the north of the Red Deer River. They occur in sediments deposited in the northern Yukon Territory during the same period, about 65 million years ago. These sediments also accumulated on a floodplain, and contain fossil pollen and spores of plants that grew in hardwood forests. Among these were ferns, tupelos, cycads, and abundant air-plants. The region was located some 500 miles north of the Arctic Circle of that time. The plants would have become dormant during the long period of seasonal darkness in order to survive, and the dinosaurs, which depended on their sight to find food, must have migrated to more southerly regions.

A thousand miles south of the Red Deer River, beyond the newly-formed ranges of mountains dividing Wyoming in a northwest-southeasterly direction, lay another ancient floodplain, which extended 700 miles farther south into what is now Mexico. Here fossil pollen and spores indicate the presence of plants requiring moist tropical environments in which to grow. The dinosaur faunas of this region are not well known, but, in addition to the duckbilled dinosaurs, horned dinosaurs and tyrannosaurs characteristic of the more northerly regions, were gigantic brontosaur-like forms. These plant-eating dinosaurs had elongated necks and tails, and occurred throughout the tropical regions of the world. The North American representative, which has been named *Alamosaurus,* is known from central Utah and from trans-Pecos Texas, near the Big Bend of the Rio Grande.

Sixty-five million years ago, dinosaurs are known to have been distributed from the Yukon Territory to Texas. A few skeletons of duckbilled dinosaurs indicate their presence on the Atlantic and Pacific seaboards of the continent as well. Indeed, dinosaurs occurred throughout the world at this time. Yet, approximately 64 million years ago this mighty race of reptiles abruptly ceased to exist. Most of us consider dinosaurs to have been clumsy colossi that somehow in the nature of things had become obsolete, their failure to survive being simply a consequence of this obsolescence. When one reviews the previous history of dinosaurs in the western interior of our continent, as outlined in earlier chapters, can such an obsolescence be seen as the cause of their sudden demise? Or is something lacking in our understanding of their history? Much thought has been given to the problem of the extinction of the dinosaurs since earth scientists first became aware that these giant reptiles once inhabited the earth.

VI The End of an Era

Continental sediments deposited at the end of the age of reptiles in the western interior of North America. The lines indicate the horizon of the extinctions.

On the Land

The air is hot and dry. The forelimb of a *Triceratops* is partly exposed on a saddle between two small hills in the badlands. It is weathering out of the siltstones in which it was buried as the earth revolved around the sun some 64 million times. When the sun had last shone upon the *Triceratops* forelimb, the bones were slowly decomposing on a humid forest floor, to where it had been dragged by a pair of squabbling young tyrannosaurs. It was then buried in silts and clays left behind by the high waters of the wet season. After the bones were covered by two feet of sediment, a marsh formed over the area where the *Triceratops* limb was buried. The plant debris that accumulated in the marsh is now visible as a purplish-brown streak forming a contour around the two small hills, just above the disintegrating bones. Within the plant debris are preserved the spores of ferns that grew in the open wetland. Fossil pollen of bald cypresses, screw pines, large-leaved gunneras, boxes, proteas, elms, and many varieties of mistletoe and unknown plants are also present in the plant debris. The marsh was then filled with silts and clays similar to those in which the *Triceratops* limb was buried, and the forest spread over the area once again.

When the *Triceratops* limb had been covered by ten feet of bluish, clayey sediment, there was a change in the pattern of sedimentation. This is represented by a coal bed about one foot thick, which can be traced around the two hills above, parallel to the purplish-brown streak of the marsh. At the base of the coal, just as the swamp was becoming established, the brownish siltstones have yielded the spores of sphagnum moss and ferns and the pollen of screw pines, alders, elms, and several unknown broad-leaved trees. The surface of the ground was moist, and the presence of subtropical ferns and screw pines indicates that the climate was warm. Yet the pollens of gunneras, mistletoes, proteas, and several other kinds of plants do not occur at the base of the coal. Above the coal, the sediments become coarser-grained and are more laminated in appearance. The larger hill is ringed by two more coal seams above the lowest one. No fragment of a dinosaur bone can be found on the higher slopes of this hill. The mystery of the extinction of the dinosaurs is locked within the sediments of these two barren hillocks, lost within badlands bathed in the heat waves of the summer sun, half a mile above the level of the sea and a thousand miles from its nearest shore.

Throughout the badlands of the western interior where skeletal elements of *Triceratops* and its contemporaries are found, broken pieces of dinosaur bone can occasionally be seen weathering out of the hillsides. However, they never occur above the base of the lowest of a series of coal seams, corresponding to the level at which the sediments become laminated and more coarse-grained. Neither can the fossil leaves, pollen and spores of many different kinds of plants be found above this level. Apparently all of the 11 major kinds of dinosaurs and nearly half of the plant species present ceased to exist in the western interior at about the same time. Forty-one varieties of crocodiles, lizards and turtles are known to have lived with these dinosaurs, but the remains of only 26 have been found in the sediments above the basal coal. It would appear that about half of the small furred mammals also disappeared, including most of the opossum-like forms.

Sediment samples containing microscopic pollen grains are more easily collected than are the skeletons of ancient animals. Moreover, fossil spores and pollen are abundantly preserved in these sediments, and an assemblage of these microfossils occurring in sediments that also contain *Triceratops* bones can be readily distinguished from those occurring at the base of the lowest coal seam or in the sediments immediately above. So far, these two pollen assemblages have been collected from levels only three to ten feet apart in the sediments. In terms of the average rate of sediment accumulation in different parts of the western interior at that time, this thickness of sediment represents a time span of between 10,000 and 50,000 years. The change in pollen assemblages, therefore, probably took place during a period of less than 10,000 years, and perhaps considerably faster. What kinds of environmental changes could have eliminated, within 10,000 years, half of the varieties of living things visible to man from an area of coastal floodplains at least a quarter of a million square miles in extent? . . . and have left no trace as would floods or glaciation? Why did the missing varieties not repopulate the floodplains from surrounding areas? . . . or was the entire continent similarly affected?

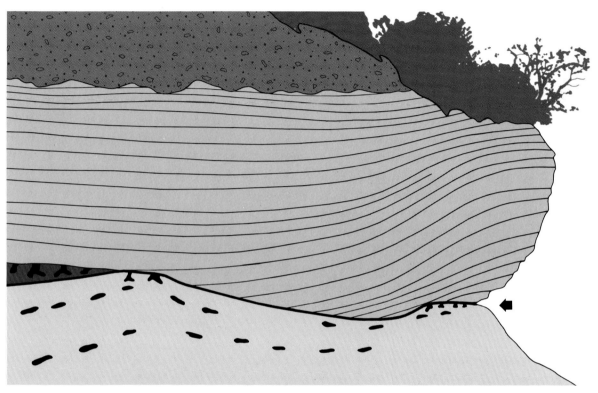

Shallow marine sediments deposited at the end of the age of reptiles in southern Scandinavia. The arrow indicates the horizon of the extinctions.

In the Sea

Cries of gulls briefly pierce the cool air and are then lost in the scent of salt water and the sound of wavelets washing the beach. The sun, rising out of the Baltic, brilliantly illuminates the chalks of the cliff of Stevns, which are exposed for several miles around a headland of the island of Sjaelland, 30 miles south of Copenhagen. The soft white chalks at the base of the sea cliff were formed 64 million years ago from a slow rain of microscopic platelets shed by tiny single-celled plants floating in the upper waters of a much more ancient sea. At that time the sea bottom lay in dim light several hundred feet below the surface. Large flat-shelled clams were scattered across the soft limey floor, and isolated sea lilies and sponges grew on their abandoned shells. All of these creatures fed on tiny organisms that they filtered from the teeming waters of the warm sea. Clouds of small fish and squid-like creatures passed overhead, and groups of larger straight-shelled baculites with tentacled heads, along with related coiled forms, were suspended in the water among clumps of sea lilies or sponges. From time to time one would be seized by a giant marine lizard during a dive, and the living creature would be crushed from its shell and swallowed in a veil of ink.

Higher on the sea cliff, the white chalk contains tiny colonial marine organisms called bryozoans, or moss-animals. These were attached to seaweeds that grew in water less than 100 feet deep, where the sunlight was more intense. The ancient sea was shoaling, and surface waves began to disturb the soft sediment below. Broad, shallow undulations formed on the sea floor. Then the rain of microscopic platelets from the tiny floating plants suddenly ceased. A thin, dark clay, in which the bones and scales of fish are imbedded, accumulated in the low troughs between the ripple crests. As the rain of platelets slowly began to fall again, a limey mud filled the troughs. It contains the remains of only a few varieties of microscopic organisms, and no shells at all of the large clams or tentacled shellfish. The time span represented by the line separating the highest layer of soft white chalk and the lowest layer of the fish clay is probably considerably less than 10,000 years.

When the limey mud had partly filled the troughs, the sea became so shallow that it covered the region only during high tide. The crests of the ripples were eroded away, and sea urchins and crustaceans made burrows in the limey mud and soft chalk. The surface of the sediments became as hard as cement through exposure to the air between tides. Then the area once again fell beneath the sea.

The hard blue limestone at the top of the cliff of Stevns contains the abundant remains of bryozoan colonies that flourished among the seaweeds, but, like the shellfish, most of the floating single-celled plants and animals had vanished.

Just as pollen occurs abundantly in sediments deposited on land, so also are the platelets and shells of tiny floating marine organisms abundantly present in sediments deposited on the bottoms of shallow seas surrounding the continents. Under appropriate conditions, they may even be preserved in sediments deposited in deep oceanic basins. The tiny plants inhabit only the uppermost levels of the oceans, where they can capture energy from the sun through the process of photosynthesis. Like their counterparts on land, these plants are the ultimate source of food for the creatures of the sea. They occur in astronomic numbers, and are grazed upon by microscopic animals, which in turn are consumed by larger forms and, finally, during the dinosaurian era, by the largest sharks and marine reptiles.

All together the platelets of 130 different varieties of these tiny plants are known around the world from sediments that also contain the remains of the last of the peculiar marine shellfish, giant swimming lizards, and bizarre long-necked plesiosaurs. One hundred and twenty-six of these varieties apparently disappear at a bedding plane in accumulations of marine sediments of that time, and only ten varieties are known from marine sediments immediately above this horizon. Many other kinds of marine organisms are not known above the horizon, or are not as diverse as they formerly were. It would appear that some kind of environmental stress, or combination of stresses, exterminated many living things in the oceans in a very short span of geologic time. Yet the surface waters of the oceans were warm soon after this event, and the rain of platelets from growing plants was about as dense as it had once been.

The Testimony of the Earth
Over much of the area drained by the upper Missouri River, the last sediments that contain the bones of *Triceratops* are rich in volcanic ash. This was carried by wind and running water from volcanoes in the western mountains, across the recently formed coal swamps on the floodplain, and into the sea in North Dakota. Then, as the hard-

ened chalk surface with its burrows slipped beneath the sea thousands of miles away in Denmark, the easternmost edge of the floodplain began to founder. In the marine muds overlying the ash-rich sediments of the floodplain occur the shells of microscopic marine animals identical to those in the limestone above the fish clay in the cliff of Stevns.

The bones and eggs of giant brontosaurs and at least five other varieties of dinosaurs have been collected from red sandstones and clays in southern France and northern Spain. These sediments were deposited under tropical conditions on land close to the level of the sea. As the sea spread south from the Bay of Biscay, lakes were formed in what is now the region of the Cantabrian Mountains in northern Spain. Within the limey muds on the lake bottoms were buried the shells of a peculiar assemblage of shellfish, including those of a very large freshwater snail. Shallow marine waters then covered the region. The microscopic shells of floating marine organisms that fell upon the lake

deposits and red beds forming the floor of the sea are identical to those in the limestones above the fish clay in Sjaelland.

Thus, the few varieties of microscopic marine organisms that occur above the fish clay in Denmark also occur above sediments containing bones of the last dinosaurs in both North Dakota and Spain. Their tiny shells are found in sediments immediately above those containing abundant remains of the marine organisms that disappeared in such widely separated areas as the Grand Banks of Newfoundland and the lands bordering the western shore of the Caspian Sea; the South Island of New Zealand and the west coast of Greenland; and the Atlantic coast of Brazil and the interior of Egypt. It would seem that a wave of extinctions swept the planet at the end of the dinosaurian era.

Did these extinctions, which nowhere seem to have lasted more than 10,000 years, occur everywhere at the same point in time? Unfortunately, existing methods for measuring the duration of events that happened so long ago are relatively imprecise. Measurements based on the rate of decay of radioactive elements are only accurate to within 2 million years for this period. By carefully examining the shapes of the shells of certain marine shellfish, such as

those of *Baculites,* which changed, or evolved, at a relatively rapid rate, time differences of the order of half a million years can easily be distinguished. It would appear that the extinctions must have occurred everywhere within a span of less than a few hundred thousand years. Otherwise, obvious differences would be detectable in the shapes of the shells of the last surviving shellfish of the dinosaurian era in different regions of the globe.

In the near future it should be possible to further refine our estimates of the duration of the extinctions throughout the world. As was noted in Chapter II, the magnetic field of the earth leaves a "print" in magnetically sensitive minerals in the rocks of the earth's crust. It is known that the magnetic field has often reversed its direction in the past, so that during certain periods the "north" indicator of a compass would point in a southerly direction. The time required for a reversal is between 1,000 and 4,000 years, or less. By noting the direction of the magnetic imprints in sediments near the horizon of the extinctions, it may be possible to determine whether or not the duration of the extinctions was about the same.

For the present, one is left with some very curious information about the extinction of the dinosaurs. Many other kinds of living things vanished with them, and the proportion that disappeared was equally great on the land and in the sea. The extinctions circled the globe, and extended from pole to pole in both hemispheres. They probably occurred in a span of less than a few hundred thousand years. In the following 64 million years, down to historic times, there have been no extinctions of comparable importance. Even during the last 2 million years, when half of the North American continent was covered by a sheet of ice, when ocean levels rose and fell several hundred feet in harmony with the thawing and freezing of continental ice sheets, and when human hunters finally depleted the large game animals surviving south of the last glacial front; even under these rapid and severe environmental stresses, the extinctions seem to have been neither so numerous, so all-pervasive, nor so sudden.

The sediments have thus far yielded little additional information. Many corals and coral-like forms and many tiny animals adapted to floating in tropical seas vanished.

The giant reptiles that inhabited the land and the seas suggest warm environments, and these too disappeared. Indeed, the platelets of the tiny floating plants suddenly began to dissolve before reaching the ocean floor in many regions where they had previously accumulated in thick, limey oozes. Perhaps the waters suddenly became cooler at these depths, or somehow became slightly more acid. Yet several subtropical varieties of plants survived in the western interior of North America, and palms continued to grow in Greenland. The changes in sea level and in the elevation of mountains were smaller when the dinosaurs died than they have been during the last million years, as continental ice sheets formed and melted. Where, in the sedimentary record, is there evidence of planet-wide crustal disturbances profound enough to bring about the disappearance of the dinosaurs and so many other organisms?

From the Depths of Space

Many suggestions have been made to explain the extinction of the dinosaurs. None of them are widely accepted among researchers familiar with the problem, and some are unacceptable because they do not consider the simultaneous disappearance of many other organisms in all environments throughout the globe. We do not know why the dinosaurs died, nor would we have been able to predict their imminent extinction through an examination of their previous history. However, several general avenues of approach to the problem are being examined. They include searches for: trace elements or other vital substances whose depletion would trigger a planet-wide collapse of plant and animal communities; indications of changes in the shape of the earth's surface that would affect wind and water currents, bringing about a sudden worldwide climatic change; and evidence demonstrating that the extinctions were neither so rapid nor so all-pervasive as has been supposed. The remarks that follow, therefore, represent but one of several lines of investigation currently under study.

The environment of space in which the earth is situated is strongly affected by the presence of a nearby star, the sun. The earth is warmed by electromagnetic radiation from the sun. Its heat drives the weather systems and ocean currents of the planet. Life on Earth is fed from electromagnetic radiation in the form of sunlight, which is captured by green plants. Other kinds of electromagnetic and cosmic radiation affect the genetic material of living things, promoting the appearance of new forms of life on the planet. Were it not for an extraterrestrial source of energy the earth would be a frozen ball, devoid of life as we know it. There is no record of crustal events on the surface of the earth during the time the dinosaurs died that would have caused worldwide extinctions over an interval of several hundred thousand years or less. Yet living things are profoundly influenced by electromagnetic radiation reaching them across the emptiness of space. So is the climate of the earth. In the apparent absence of unprecedented crustal disturbances, it may be useful to consider the extraterrestrial environment.

Life flourishes on Earth within certain narrow limits of light and heat, given an otherwise suitable environment on the planetary surface. This would soon become obvious to anyone attempting to grow tomatoes in the shade of his neighbour's Lombardy poplar, or expecting to obtain fruit from fig trees grown out of doors in eastern Ontario. Both are possible, but difficult. Because our region of space is so intensely bathed in the light and heat of the sun, any sudden and substantial change in the sun's radiation would dramat-

ically affect life on Earth. However, the sun was formed nearly 5,000 million years ago, and, according to present estimates, should continue to radiate energy at a constant rate for an equal length of time to come. Although the sun may experience major instabilities, there is no available evidence that it has done so, and the sun is considered to be a very stable star.

Just as the earth revolves around the sun, so also does the sun revolve around the centre of the galaxy. The spacial environments the sun traverses in the course of its revolution, requiring between 200 million and 280 million years, are not uniform. Every 80 million to 90 million years the sun's orbit crosses the region of the galactic "equator", where cosmic

radiation is concentrated by the galactic magnetic field. During the time of the sun's "equatorial crossing", background radiation levels would rise on the surface of the earth. However, they would probably not increase sufficiently to damage living things, and resulting environmental changes would endure for a much longer period than the several hundred thousand years, or less, during which the extinctions took place at the end of the dinosaurian era.

However, some areas of the galactic environment may be profoundly affected by colossal stellar explosions called supernovae. At a rate of about one per hundred years per galaxy, a star will suddenly become more luminous. Within a few days it will shine with an intensity comparable to that of a thousand million suns, and for a few weeks it may surpass an entire galaxy in brightness. The star then gradually fades, leaving behind a great pulse of electromagnetic radiation expanding at the speed of light, more slowly expanding envelopes of cosmic radiation and gas, and, occasionally, an extremely dense stellar remnant. These explosions have been observed with the naked eye nine times during the last 2,000 years. The "guest stars", as they were called by the ancients, are brilliant yellow-orange objects that shine with pointed rays and are so bright that at night objects can be seen by their light. They often remain visible at midday.

The guest stars of the ancients were too far away to affect terrestrial environments. However, by observing the rate at which supernovae occur in galaxies, and counting remnants of their occurrence near the sun, it is calculated that the solar system should be in a region of space near a supernova on an average of once every 50 million years. This being so, it is probable that the earth has been briefly immersed in waves of high-energy radiation comparable to those occurring near powerful thermonuclear explosions. It is also possible that short-term climatic changes would have occurred simultaneously.

At present, only two lines of evidence tend to imply that the earth was indeed struck 64 million years ago by a wave of high-energy radiation from a supernova. The first of these are the extinctions themselves. The vulnerability of living things to excessive radiation and the brevity and global extent of the extinctions that occurred at that time are in apparent conformity with a brief but drastic environmental change on the earth. The second lies in the recent discovery of an enormous ring of interstellar gas, some 18,000 billion miles in diameter, near the solar system in space. Its present speed of expansion indicates that the ring was created in an explosion that occurred relatively close to the sun about 65 million years ago. Associated with the ring of gas is an envelope of interstellar dust and young stars that have condensed from the dust and gas swept up in the explosion. These are evidently the remains of one of the most powerful kinds of supernovae known.

As the physical properties of supernovae are better understood it should be possible to examine the sedimentary record for evidence of such an event. It is probable that radioactive elements created in the atmosphere by relatively far-off supernovae have been detected in marine sediments that were deposited at two different times less than half a million years ago. The sediments that were deposited when the dinosaurs died could be examined for similarly created elements. The climatic effects of the arrival of a large amount of electromagnetic and cosmic radiation in the atmosphere could also be studied. The duration of the extinctions can possibly be more accurately defined by comparing the sedimentary record of this event to that of reversals in the earth's magnetic field of approximately the same age. We should know in the near future whether or not the dinosaurs disappeared as a consequence of a colossal stellar explosion in nearby space.

The nature of the environmental crisis that swept the globe 64 million years ago remains obscure. Nevertheless, in spite of its apparent severity, a large proportion of the plants and animals inhabiting the earth survived the crisis. The ecosystems of the earth did not quickly heal, and at least ten million years elapsed before the plant and animal communities recovered much of their former diversity. The

A waning supernova over a dead
Ankylosaurus *in a broken, frozen*
forest

world, however, remained warm, much warmer than it is now. On the land, flowering plants and birds continued to increase and diversify, as they had begun to do during the dinosaurian era. The mammals blossomed into a host of new forms after the dinosaurs had gone. New varieties of tiny floating organisms repopulated the seas, and the oceans again abounded with many varieties of living things. The biological systems of our planet are incomprehensibly wonderful in their simplicity and complexity. And the greatest wonder among them is the human mind, when guided to work in harmony with the fabric of nature and its own being.

The dinosaurs are indeed dead. The sight of their bronze skeletons in the darkened galleries of our museums seems to call to us hauntingly. They too were wonderful, they are dead, and their death recalls to us something of the meaning of living. Their giant skeletons embody the abundance of a long-vanished world. The life of our planet has more than recovered from the forces that destroyed the world in which they lived. Yet, would we have survived had we been in their place?

References

Chapter I

Colbert, E.H. 1968. *Men and dinosaurs, the search in field and laboratory.* Dutton, New York. 283 pp.

Douglas, R.J.W. 1969. *Geological map of Canada.* Geological Survey of Canada Map 1250A, scale 1: 5,000,000.

Irish, E.J.W. 1971. *Geology, southern plains of Alberta.* Geological Survey of Canada Map 1286A, scale 1: 500,000.

Ostrom, J.H., and McIntosh, J.S. 1966. *Marsh's dinosaurs.* Yale University Press, New Haven, Conn., and London. 388 pp.

Prest, V.K. 1969. *Retreat of Wisconsin and Recent ice in North America.* Geological Survey of Canada Map 1257A, scale 1: 5,000,000.

Russell, D.A., and Chamney, T.P. 1967. *Notes on the biostratigraphy of dinosaurian and microfossil faunas in the Edmonton Formation of Alberta.* National Museum of Canada, Natural History Papers 35. 22 pp.

Russell, L.S. 1966. *Dinosaur hunting in western Canada.* Royal Ontario Museum, Life Sciences Contribution 70. 37 pp.

Stockwell, C.H. 1969. *Tectonic map of Canada.* Geological Survey of Canada Map 1251A, scale 1: 5,000,000.

Whitaker, S.H., and Pearson, D.E. 1972. *Geological map of Saskatchewan.* Saskatchewan Department of Mineral Resources and Saskatchewan Research Council, scale 1: 267,200.

Chapter II

Balkwill, H.R. 1971. *Reconnaissance geology, southern Great Bear Plain, District of Mackenzie.* Geological Survey of Canada, Paper 71-11. 47 pp.

Bell, W.A. 1957. *Flora of the Upper Cretaceous Nanaimo Group of Vancouver Island, British Columbia.* Geological Survey of Canada, Memoir 293. 84 pp.

Brown, C.A. 1945. *Louisiana trees and shrubs.* Louisiana Forestry Commission Bulletin, No. 1. 262 pp.

Caldwell, W.G.E. 1968. *The late Cretaceous Bearpaw Formation in the South Saskatchewan River Valley.* Saskatchewan Research Council, Geology Division, Report No. 8. 86 pp.

Couillard, R., and Irving, E. 1973. Reversals of the geomagnetic field and the palaeolatitude of North America during the Cretaceous Period [abstract]. Page 34 in *Colloquium on the Cretaceous System in the western interior of North America.* Geological Association of Canada Special Paper.

Gill, J.R., and Cobban, W.A. 1966. *The Red Bird section of the Upper Cretaceous Pierre Shale in Wyoming.* U.S. Geological Survey, Professional Paper 393-A. 73 pp.

———— 1973. *Stratigraphy and geologic history of the Montana Group and equivalent rocks, Montana, Wyoming, North and South Dakota.* U.S. Geological Survey, Professional Paper 776. 37 pp.

Hosie, R.C. 1969. *Native trees of Canada.* 7th ed. Queen's Printer, Ottawa. 380 pp.

Jeletzky, J.A. 1971. *Marine Cretaceous biotic provinces and paleogeography of western and arctic Canada: illustrated by a detailed study of ammonites.* Geological Survey of Canada, Paper 70-22. 92 pp.

Mallory, W.W., ed. 1972. *Geologic Atlas of the Rocky Mountain Region, United States of America.* Rocky Mountain Association of Geologists, Denver, Colo. 331 pp.

McCrossan, R.G., and Glaister, R.P., eds. 1966. *Geological history of western Canada.* 2d ed. Alberta Society of Petroleum Geologists, Calgary, Alta. 232 pp.

Norton, N.J., and Hall, J.W. 1969. Palynology of the Upper Cretaceous and Lower Tertiary in the type locality of the Hell Creek Formation, Montana, U.S.A. *Palaeontographica* 125 (B): 1–64.

Pitman, W.C., III, and Talwani, M. 1972. Sea-floor spreading in the North Atlantic. *Geological Society of America Bulletin* 83: 619–46.

Russell, D.A. 1973. The environments of Canadian dinosaurs. *Canadian Geographical Journal* 87: 4–11.

Scott, J.R., and Cobban, W.A. 1965. *Geologic and biostratigraphic map of the Pierre Shale between Jarre Creek and Loveland, Colorado.* U.S. Geological Survey Map I-439, scale 1: 48,000.

Smiley, C.J. 1969. Cretaceous floras of Chandler–Colville Region, Alaska: stratigraphy and preliminary floristics. *American Association of Petroleum Geologists Bulletin* 53: 482–502.

Snead, R.G. 1969. *Microfloral diagnosis of the Cretaceous–Tertiary boundary, central Alberta.* Research Council of Alberta, Bulletin 25. 148 pp.

Strivastava, S.K. 1969. Pollen biostratigraphy and paleoecology of the Edmonton Formation, Alberta, Canada. *Palaeogeography, Palaeoclimatology, Palaeoecology* 7: 221–76.

Williams, G.D., and Stelk, C.R. 1973. Speculations on the Cretaceous paleogeography of North America [abstract]. Page 51 in *Colloquium on the Cretaceous System in the western interior of North America.* Geological Association of Canada Special Paper.

Wolfe, J.A. 1971. Tertiary climatic fluctuations and methods of analysis of Tertiary floras. *Palaeogeography, Palaeoclimatology, Palaeoecology* 9: 27–57.

Chapter III

Bakker, R.T. 1971. Dinosaurian physiology and the origin of mammals. *Evolution* 25: 636–58 (see also discussion in *Evolution* 27: 166–74; 28: 491–504).

Bell, W.A. 1949. *Uppermost Cretaceous and Paleocene floras of western Alberta.* Geological Survey of Canada Bulletin 13. 231 pp.

————— 1965. *Upper Cretaceous and Paleocene plants of western Canada.* Geological Survey of Canada Paper 65-35. 46 pp.

Boreske, J.R., Jr. 1974. *A review of the North American fossil Amiid fishes.* Bulletin of the Museum of Comparative Zoology 146 (1). 87 pp.

Colbert, E.H. 1962. *The weights of dinosaurs.* American Museum Novitates, No. 2076. 16 pp.

Coombs, W.P., Jr. 1971. The Ankylosauria. Ph.D. dissertation, Columbia University. 487 pp.

Delevoryas, T. 1964. Two petrified angiosperms from the Upper Cretaceous of South Dakota. *Journal of Paleontology* 38: 584–86.

Dodson, P. 1971. Sedimentology and taphonomy of the Oldman Formation (Campanian), Dinosaur Provincial Park, Alberta (Canada). *Palaeogeography, Palaeoclimatology, Palaeoecology* 10: 21–74.

Erickson, B.R. 1972. *The lepidosaurian reptile* Champsosaurus *in North America.* Science Museum of Minnesota, Saint Paul (Monograph: paleontology, vol. 1). 91 pp.

Fox, R.C. 1970. A bibliography of Cretaceous and Tertiary vertebrates from western Canada. *Bulletin of Canadian Petroleum Geology* 18: 263–81. [This bibliography contains many references to descriptions of the Cretaceous backboned animals of western Canada that have not been included here.]

Heaton, M.J. 1972. The palatal structure of some Canadian Hadrosauridae. *Canadian Journal of Earth Sciences* 9: 185–205.

Jeletzky, J.A. 1971. *See* references for Chapter II.

Johnson, H., and Storer, J.E. 1974. *A guide to Alberta vertebrate fossils from the age of dinosaurs.* Provincial Museum of Alberta, Publication No. 4. 129 pp.

Lambe, L.M. 1902. On vertebrata of the mid-Cretaceous of the North-western Territory. *Geological Survey of Canada, Contributions to Canadian Palaeontology* 3 (2): 25–81.

McAlpine, J.F., and Martin, J.E.H. 1969. Canadian amber. *Beaver,* summer 1969: 28–37.

McLean, J.R. 1971. *Stratigraphy of the Upper Cretaceous Judith River Formation in the Canadian Great Plains.* Saskatchewan Research Council, Geology Division, Report No. 11. 96 pp.

Ostrom, J.H. 1966. Functional morphology and evolution of the ceratopsian dinosaurs. *Evolution* 20: 290–308.

Ramanujam, C.G.K. 1972. Fossil coniferous wood from the Oldman Formation of Alberta. *Canadian Journal of Botany* 50: 595–602.

Richmond, N.D. 1965. Perhaps juvenile dinosaurs were always scarce. *Journal of Paleontology* 39: 503–05.

Russell, D.A. 1967. *A census of dinosaur specimens collected in western Canada.* National Museum of Canada, Natural History Papers 36. 13 pp.

———— 1969. A new specimen of *Stenonychosaurus* from the Oldman Formation of Alberta. *Canadian Journal of Earth Sciences* 6: 595–612.

———— 1970. *Tyrannosaurs from the late Cretaceous of western Canada.* National Museums of Canada, Publications in Palaeontology, No. 1. 34 pp.

———— 1972. A pterosaur from the Oldman Formation of Alberta. *Canadian Journal of Earth Sciences* 9: 1338–40.

Russell, L.S. 1964. *Cretaceous non-marine faunas of northwestern North America.* Royal Ontario Museum, Life Sciences Contribution 61. 24 pp.

Sahni, A. 1972. The vertebrate fauna of the Judith River Formation, Montana. *Bulletin of the American Museum of Natural History* 147: 321–412.

Spotilla, J.R., Lommen, P.W., Bakken, G.S., and Gates, D.M. 1973. A mathematical model for body temperature of large reptiles: implications for dinosaur ecology. *American Naturalist* 107: 391–404.

Sternberg, C.M. 1950. *Notes on the dinosaur quarries, Steveville, Alberta.* Geological Survey of Canada Map 969A, scale 1: 31,680.

Storer, J.E., and Johnson, H. 1974. *Ischyrhiza* (Chondrichthyes: Pristidae) from the Upper Cretaceous Foremost Formation of Alberta. *Canadian Journal of Earth Sciences* 11: 712–15.

Waldman, M., and Hopkins, W.S., Jr. 1970. Coprolites from the Upper Cretaceous of Alberta, with a description of their microflora. *Canadian Journal of Earth Sciences* 7: 1295–303.

Chapter IV

Bell, W.A. 1949; 1965. *See* references for Chapter III.

Brown, C.A. 1945. *See* references for Chapter II.

Caldwell, W.G.E. 1968. *See* references for Chapter II.

Ferguson, D.K. 1967. On the phytogeography of Coniferales in the European Cenozoic. *Palaeogeography, Palaeoclimatology, Palaeoecology* 3: 73–110.

Hosie, R.C. 1969. *See* references for Chapter II.

Irish, E.J.W. 1970. The Edmonton Group of south-central Alberta. *Bulletin of Canadian Petroleum Geology* 18: 125–55.

———— and Havard, C.J. 1968. *The Whitemud and Battle Formations ("Kneehills Tuff Zone") a stratigraphic marker.* Geological Survey of Canada, Paper 67-63. 51 pp.

Jeletzky, J.A. 1971. *See* references for Chapter II.

Kramers, J.W., and Mellon, G.B. 1972. Upper Cretaceous–Paleocene coal-bearing strata, northwest-central Alberta plains. *Research Council of Alberta, Information Series* 60: 109–24.

Kräusel, R. 1922. Die Nahrung von Trachodon. *Palaeontologische Zeitschrift* 4: 80.

Langston, W., Jr. 1967. The thick-headed ceratopsian dinosaur *Pachyrhinosaurus* from the Edmonton Formation near Drumheller, Canada. *Canadian Journal of Earth Sciences* 4: 171–86.

Rozhdestvenskii, A.K. 1960. *Chasse aux dinosaures dans le désert de Gobi.* Librairie Arthème Fayard, Paris. 301 pp.

Russell, D.A. 1972. Ostrich dinosaurs from the late Cretaceous of western Canada. *Canadian Journal of Earth Sciences* 9: 375–402.

———— and Chamney, T.P. 1967. *See* references for Chapter I.

Shepheard, W.W., and Hills, L.V. 1970. Depositional environments, Bearpaw–Horseshoe Canyon (Upper Cretaceous) transition zone, Drumheller "Badlands", Alberta. *Bulletin of Canadian Petroleum Geology* 18: 166–215.

Srivastava, S.K. 1969. *See* references for Chapter II.

Steiner, J., Williams, G.D., and Dickie, G.J. 1972. Coal deposits of the Alberta plains. *Research Council of Alberta, Information Series* 60: 85–108.

Tozer, E.T. 1956. *Uppermost Cretaceous and Paleocene non-marine molluscan faunas of western Alberta.* Geological Survey of Canada, Memoir 280. 125 pp.

Chapter V

Bell, R.E. 1965. Geology and stratigraphy of the Fort Peck fossil field, northwest McCone County, Montana. Master's thesis, University of Minnesota. 166 pp.

Bell, W.A. 1949. *See* references for Chapter III.

Binda, P.L., and Lerbekmo, J.F. 1973. Grain-size distribution and depositional environment of Whitemud Sandstones, Edmonton Formation (Upper Cretaceous), Alberta, Canada. *Bulletin of Canadian Petroleum Geology* 21: 52–80.

Brown, R.W. 1939. Fossil plants from the Colgate Member of the Fox Hills Sandstone and adjacent strata. *U.S. Geological Survey, Professional Paper* 189-I: 239–75.

———— 1962. *Paleocene flora of the Rocky Mountains and Great Plains.* U.S. Geological Survey, Professional Paper 375. 119 pp.

Byers, P.N. 1969. Mineralogy and origin of the upper Eastend and Whitemud Formations of south-central and southwestern Saskatchewan and southeastern Alberta. *Canadian Journal of Earth Sciences* 6: 317–34.

Campbell, J.D. 1967. *Ardley Coal Zone in the Alberta Plains: central Red Deer River area.* Research Council of Alberta, Report 67-1. 28 pp.

Colbert, E.H. 1961. *Dinosaurs, their discovery and their world.* Dutton, New York. 300 pp.

Estes, R.D. 1964. Fossil vertebrates from the late Cretaceous Lance Formation, eastern Wyoming. *University of California Publications in Geological Sciences* 49. 180 pp.

———— and Berberian, P. 1970. *Paleoecology of a late Cretaceous vertebrate community from Montana.* Breviora (U.S.), No. 343. 35 pp.

Frye, C.I. 1969. *Stratigraphy of the Hell Creek Formation in North Dakota.* North Dakota Geological Survey Bulletin 54. 65 pp.

Gill, J.R., and Cobban, W.A. 1973. *See* references for Chapter II.

Gilmore, C.W. 1946. *Reptilian fauna of the North Horn Formation of central Utah.* U.S. Geological Survey, Professional Paper 210-C. 53 pp.

Irish, E.J.W., and Havard, C.J. 1968. *See* references for Chapter IV.

Jeletzky, J.A. 1971. *See* references for Chapter II.

Jensen, F.S., and Varnes, H.D. 1964. *Geology of the Fort Peck area, Garfield, McCone and Valley counties, Montana.* U.S. Geological Survey, Professional Paper 414-F. 49 pp.

Kupsch, W.O. 1956. *Geology of the eastern Cypress Hills.* Saskatchewan Department of Mineral Resources, Report No. 20. 30 pp.

Lillegraven, J.A. 1969. *Latest Cretaceous mammals of upper part of Edmonton Formation of Alberta, Canada, and review of marsupial placental dichotomy in mammalian evolution.* University of Kansas Paleontological Contributions, Article 50. 122 pp.

Mallory, W.W., ed. 1972. *See* references for Chapter II.

North, B.R., and Caldwell, W.G.E. 1970. *Foraminifera from the late Cretaceous Bearpaw Formation in the South Saskatchewan River Valley.* Saskatchewan Research Council, Geology Division, Report No. 9. 117 pp.

Norton, N.J., and Hall, J.W. 1969. *See* references for Chapter II.

Rouse, G.E., and Srivastava, S.K. 1972. Palynological zonation of Cretaceous and early Tertiary rocks of the Bonnet Plume Formation, northeastern Yukon, Canada. *Canadian Journal of Earth Sciences* 9: 1163–79.

Russell, D.A. 1967. *See* references for Chapter III.

———— 1970. The dinosaurs of central Asia. *Canadian Geographical Journal* 81: 208–15.

———— 1973. *See* references for Chapter II.

———— 1975. Late Cretaceous larger reptiles. *In* E.G. Kauffman and W.A. Cobban, eds., *Cretaceous biostratigraphy, western interior United States and southern Canada.* Geological Society of America Bulletin [in press].

Russell, L.S. 1948. *The geology of the southern part of the Cypress Hills, southwestern Saskatchewan.* Saskatchewan Department of Mineral Resources, Report No. 8. 60 pp.

Shoemaker, R.E. 1966. Fossil leaves of the Hell Creek and Tullock Formations of eastern Montana. *Palaeontographica* 119: 54–75.

Snead, R.G. 1969. *See* references for Chapter II.

Van Valen, L., and Sloan, R.E. 1965. The earliest primates. *Science* 150 (3697): 743–45.

Chapter VI

Erben, H.K. 1972. Ultrastrukturen und Dicke der Wand pathologischer Eischalen. *Akademie der Wissenschaften und der Literatur, Abhandlungen der mathematisch-naturwissenschaftlichen Klasse* (Mainz), Jahrgang 1972, No. 6: 193–216.

Fox, S.K., Jr., and Olsson, R.K. 1969. Danian planktonic foraminifera from the Cannonball Formation in North Dakota. *Journal of Paleontology* 43: 1397–404.

Gorenstein, P., and Tucker, W. 1971. Supernova remnants. *Scientific American* 224: 74–85.

Hallam, A. 1974. Mass extinctions in the fossil record. *Nature* (London) 251: 568–69.

Hatfield, C.B., and Camp, M.J. 1970. Mass extinctions correlated with periodic galactic events. *Geological Society of America Bulletin* 81: 911–14.

Hays, J.D., and Pittman, W.C., III. 1973. Lithospheric plate motion, sea level changes and climatic and ecological consequences. *Nature* (London) 246: 18–22.

Higdon, J.C., and Lingenfelter, R.E. 1973. Sea sediments, cosmic rays and pulsars. *Nature* (London) 246: 403–05.

Hughes, V.A., and Routledge, D. 1972. An expanding ring of interstellar gas with center close to the sun. *Astronomical Journal* 77: 210–14.

Lapparent, A.F. de. 1967. Les dinosaures de France. *Sciences* (Paris), No. 51: 4–19.

Leffingwell, H.A. 1971. Palynology of the Lance and Fort Union Formations of the type Lance area, Wyoming. *Geological Society of America Special Paper* 127: 1–64.

Lequeux, J. 1972. Quand une étoile explose. *Science, Progrès, Découverte*, No. 3449: 36–43.

Lingenfelter, R.E. 1969. Pulsars and local cosmic ray prehistory. *Nature* (London) 224: 1182–86.

Martin, P.S., and Wright, H.E., Jr., eds. 1967. *Pleistocene extinctions, the search for a cause.* Yale University Press, New Haven, Conn., and London. 452 pp.

Newell, N.D. 1971. *An outline history of tropical organic reefs.* American Museum Novitates, No. 2465. 37 pp.

Ögelman, H. 1970. Extensive air shower arrays as detectors of prompt gamma rays from supernovae explosions. *Nature* (London) 228: 1181.

Plaziat, J.-C. 1970. Conséquences stratigraphiques de l'interstratification de Rognacien dans le Maestrichtien d'Alava (Espagne). *Comptes rendus de l'Académie des Sciences* (Paris), série D, tome 270: 2768–71.

————— 1970. La limite crétacé-tertiaire en Alava méridionale. *Comptes rendus de la Société géologique de France,* fascicule 3: 77–78.

Rasmussen, H.W. 1971. Echinoid and crustacean burrows and their diagenetic significance in the Maastrichtian–Danian of Stevns Klint, Denmark. *Lethaia* 4: 191–216.

Ruderman, M.A. 1974. Possible consequences of nearby supernova explosions for atmospheric ozone and terrestrial life. *Science* (Washington, D.C.) 184: 1079–81.

Russell, D.A. 1973. Reptilian diversity and the Cretaceous–Tertiary transition in North America [abstract]. Page 44 in *Colloquium on the Cretaceous System in the western interior of North America.* Geological Association of Canada Special Paper.

————— 1975. L'extinction des sauropsidés à la fin de l'ère secondaire — une hypothèse. In *Problèmes actuels de Paléontologie.* Colloque international du Centre national de la Recherche scientifique, Paris, 1973. [In press.]

————— and Tucker, W. 1971. Supernovae and the extinction of the dinosaurs. *Nature* (London) 229: 553–54.

Shen, C.S. 1969. Pulsars and ancient Chinese records of supernovae explosions. *Nature* (London) 221: 1039–40.

Sloan, R.E. 1971. Cretaceous and Paleocene communities of western North America. Pages 427–53 *in* E.L. Yochelson, ed., *Proceedings of the North American Paleontological Convention, Chicago, 1969.* 2 vols. Allen Press, Lawrence, Kansas.

Tappan, H. 1968. Primary production, isotopes, extinctions and the atmosphere. *Palaeogeography, Palaeoclimatology, Palaeoecology* 4: 187–210.

Terry, K.D., and Tucker, W. 1967. Biologic effects of supernovae. *Science* (Washington, D.C.) 159: 421–23.

Tschudy, R.H. 1971. Palynology of the Cretaceous–Tertiary boundary in the northern Rocky Mountain and Mississippi Embayment regions. *Geological Society of America Special Paper* 127: 65–111.

Ul Haq, Bilal. 1973. Transgressions, climatic change and the diversity of calcareous nannoplankton. *Marine Geology* 15: M25–M30.

Worsley, T. 1974. The Cretaceous–Tertiary boundary event in the ocean. *Society of Economic Paleontology and Mineralogy Special Publication* 20: 94–125.

CANADIANA